The Spectrum Girl's Survival Toolkit
The Workbook for Autistic Girls

Siena Castellon

Foreword by Dr. Temple Grandin

APC
PUBLISHING
Your First Source for Practical Solutions for Autism Spectrum and Related Disorders
Exceptional Resources For Extraordinary Minds

AAPC PUBLISHING
PO Box 861116
Shawnee, KS 66218
Local Phone (913) 897-1004 Fax (913) 728-6090
www.aapcautismbooks.com

Published June 2021 by AAPC Publishing

Names: Castellon, Siena, author. | Grandin, Temple, writer of foreword.

Title: The spectrum girl's survival toolkit : the workbook for autistic girls / Siena Castellon ; foreword by Dr. Temple Grandin.

Description: Shawnee, KS : AAPC Publishing, [2021] | Includes index.

Identifiers: ISBN: 978-1-942197-42-3 (paperback)

Subjects: LCSH: Autistic girls--Handbooks, manuals, etc. | Youth with autism spectrum disorders-- Handbooks, manuals, etc. | Autism spectrum disorders-- Handbooks, manuals, etc. | Social phobia in adolescence--Handbooks, manuals, etc. | Sensory integration dysfunction-- Handbooks, manuals, etc. | Self-help techniques. | Success. | Self-esteem. | Self-acceptance. | Self-realization. | Self-actualization (Psychology) | Quality of life. | BISAC: SELF-HELP / General. | SELF-HELP / Communication & Social Skills. | SELF-HELP / Personal Growth / Success. | SELF-HELP / Journaling. | FAMILY & RELATIONSHIPS / Autism Spectrum Disorders.

Classification: LCC: RC553.A88 C37 2021 | DDC: 616.85/88200835--dc23

THE SPECTRUM GIRL'S SURVIVAL TOOLKIT

THE WORKBOOK FOR AUTISTIC GIRLS

A companion to the bestseller **The Spectrum Girl's Survival Guide,** this essential survival toolkit gives you all the coping strategies you'll need to help you overcome the challenges that may be holding you back.

Written for teen autistic girls, this fun and friendly workbook is filled with engaging, interactive exercises and practical advice on how to manage social anxiety and sensory overloads, make and maintain friendships, succeed in school, and much, much more.

ABOUT ME

My name is Siena. I recently graduated from high school and will be soon studying physics at university. At times, these achievements seemed unrealistic and overly ambitious. You see, I'm autistic, dyslexic, and dyspraxic. I also have ADHD. As I'm sure you can relate, these neurological differences made school extremely difficult. To make things worse, I struggled to find the support I needed. All the information, resources and websites I found were aimed at our parents. Being left out seemed odd to me since we're the ones that need the information and guidance the most. When I was 13, I created a website (www.QLMentoring.com) to share the tips and tricks I used to succeed in school.

It wasn't long before I also realized that there were no books written for autistic girls. All the books were written for autistic boys. Since autistic girls are very different from autistic boys, these books failed to address the unique challenges that we face. When I was 16, I wrote **The Spectrum Girl's Survival Guide: How To Grow Up Awesome and Autistic.** I set out to write the type of book I wish I could have benefited from: an uplifting survival guide filled with practical information and strategies to help autistic girls overcome their challenges and achieve their goals.

Like many autistic students, my school experience was a bumpy one. Sadly, school isn't always a welcoming place for people who are different. Our autism makes us different. Our sensory issues, social anxiety, and social challenges are experiences that set us apart.

Our classmates can't relate to us. Most of our teachers don't understand us and don't have the training to nurture and support us. As a consequence, we are frequently bullied for walking to the beat of our own drum, mostly by other students and sometimes even by our teachers. Eventually, many of us feel immense pressure to change who we are so that we can fit in and be like everyone else. But in the process of transforming into someone others will accept, it's easy for us to lose sight of who we are.

There were many times that I didn't think I would graduate from high school. Although I did well in my classes, making it through the school day was a monumental feat. Sometimes the sensory overloads caused by my school environment were debilitating. Sometimes my social anxiety got the best of me. And sometimes, my poor organizational skills threatened to derail my academic achievements. My life revolved around finding solutions to compensate for my disabilities so that the disadvantages, barriers, and challenges I faced didn't prevent me from achieving my goals. It was exhausting! At times my journey was lonely and demoralizing, made worse because things seemed to come so effortlessly and easily to everyone else.

Although I often felt isolated and alone, I took great comfort from knowing that there were millions of other young people just like me who were having similar struggles and experiences. It is estimated that 20% of all students are neurodivergent. In other words, one in every five students has a neurological difference, which means they think and learn differently. Instead of adapting the educational system to include us, the system often works against us. Many of us struggle to keep our heads above water in an environment that can feel hostile and unwelcoming. I hope to change this. I believe that everyone should be given the ingredients that they need to reach their potential.

Two years ago, I launched **Neurodiversity Celebration Week**, an international movement to change stereotypes and misconceptions about autism and learning differences. At its core, Neurodiversity Celebration Week aims to flip the narrative so that schools recognize the many strengths and talents of their autistic students and students with learning differences instead of focusing only on our weaknesses. Currently, over 1,400 schools and over 860,000 students are taking part worldwide.

In the last five years, hundreds of autistic young people have reached out to me and have entrusted me with their stories. Although I have won many prestigious international and national awards, the moments I treasure the most are reading the messages I receive from neurodivergent young people. The email from a 12-year old girl in Nigeria who read my book and is now proud to be autistic. The message from a young girl who is no longer ashamed of being autistic and is embracing who she is.

In October 2020, the United Nations selected me to be a Young Leader for the Sustainable Development Goals (SDGs). This opportunity has given me a global platform to continue advocating for autism acceptance and equality. I hope that one day soon, you and future generations of autistic youth will live in a world where we're understood, supported, and accepted. Until then, never forget that you're not alone and that you're awesome just the way you are.

Siena

Twitter: @QLMentoring / @NCWeek

Instagram: @QLMentoring

IMAGINE IF WE OBSESSED ABOUT THE THINGS WE LOVE THE MOST ABOUT OURSELVES.

TABLE OF CONTENTS

Foreword   xv

Introduction   xvii

How To Use This Book   xviii

CHAPTER 1: UNDERSTANDING YOUR EMOTIONS

Decoding Your Emotions   1

What Is Alexithymia?   2

Wheel of Emotions   3

Feelings Vocabulary   4

Name That Feeling   5

My Body's Response To My Feelings   6

My Emotion Thermometer   8

Linking My Feelings, Thoughts, and Behaviors   10

Getting To Know My Feelings   13

CHAPTER 2: EXPRESSING AND CONTROLLING YOUR EMOTIONS

Knowing My Triggers   15

What Pushes Your Buttons?   17

Connecting The Dots   18

Trigger Tracking   20

Use Your Sensory Powers   21

My Soundtrack   24

Unleash Your Imagination   26

Color-Coding My Feelings   28

Practice Gratitude   32

Random Acts of Kindness   34

CHAPTER 3: UNDERSTANDING YOUR ANXIETY

What Is Anxiety?   37

The Symptoms of Anxiety   38

Exploring Your Anxiety   40

Balancing Your Worries   45

What's The Worst That Could Happen?   47

Anxiety Fact Checking   48

Tracking My Anxiety Triggers   50

My Anxiety Thermometer   52

Healthy Coping Activities   54

CHAPTER 4: UNDERSTANDING YOUR SOCIAL ANXIETY

The Symptoms of Social Anxiety   57

Exploring Your Social Anxiety   59

The Physical Symptoms of Social Anxiety   66

Common Social Anxiety Triggers   67

How Social Anxiety Can Affect Your Life   68

Redirect Your Focus   69

Social Anxiety Fact Checking   70

Tracking My Social Anxiety Triggers   72

My Social Anxiety Thermometer   74

CHAPTER 5: UNDERSTANDING YOUR ANGER AND FRUSTRATION

The Art Of Anger Management   77

Reining In Your Anger   79

Becoming Aware of Your Anger Warning Signs   80

Exploring Your Anger   81

Getting Acquainted With Your Anger   83

Tackling Your Anger   84

Negative Though Patterns Than Can Trigger Anger   85

Give Yourself A Reality Check   86

Practice Self-Kindness And Compassion   87

CHAPTER 6: UNDERSTANDING YOUR THOUGHTS, FEELINGS, AND BEHAVIORS

Your Thoughts, Feelings, And Behaviors   89

Thoughts vs. Feelings   98

Anxiety Or Worry?   100

Anxiety Or Worry: Which Is It?   101

Worry Log   102

Let It Go   105

Escape-Aid   106

Lock Away Your Worries For Safe Keeping   107

CHAPTER 7: REFRAMING YOUR NEGATIVE THOUGHTS

Challenging Your Thinking Errors and Mix-Ups   109

Reframing Your Thoughts   114

Flipping Negative Thoughts Into Positive Thoughts   116

Controlling Your Thoughts   118

Stop - Identify - Reframe   119

Reframing Sad Thoughts   120

Test Your Thinking   121

Helping Thinking   122

Become An Optimist   123

Good News: Looking On The Bright Side   124

CHAPTER 8: HOW TO MAKE FRIENDS

Autism And Friendships   127

What Makes A True Friend?   129

Top 10 Tips For Being A Good Friend   131

What Do I Tell Myself?   136

Use Your Body Language   137

How To Start A Conversation   138

How To Keep The Conversation Going   140

How To End A Conversation   141

Top 10 Tips For A Fun Conversation   142

CHAPTER 9: HOW TO MAINTAIN FRIENDSHIPS

Top 10 Tips For Maintaining Your Friendships 145

Random Acts Of Kindness 148

Dealing With Gossip 148

Learning To Accept Constructive Criticism 150

Accepting Criticism Practice 152

The Power of "I" Statements 156

"I" Statements vs. "You" Statements 158

Different Perspectives 159

CHAPTER 10: HOW TO DEAL WITH BULLYING

What's Bullying? 161

What Does Bullying Look Like? 164

What To Do If You're Being Bullied 167

What To Do If You're Being Cyber-Bullied 170

Who's A Bystander? 172

What Can I Do If I'm A Bystander? 172

Top 10 Tips For Dealing With Being Bullied 173

Famous People Who Were Bullied 174

Getting Support 176

CHAPTER 11: RECOGNIZING YOUR STRENGTHS

Recognizing Your Strengths	179
How To Find Your Strengths	180
Identifying Your Strengths	183
Uncovering Your Strengths	184
I Am ….	186
My Strength Stories	187
Using Your Strengths	188
From Failure To Success	189
Be Motivated By Setbacks	190
My Battle Cry!	191
My Trophy Collection	192
Mirror, Mirror	193

CHAPTER 12: HOW TO SUCCEED IN SCHOOL

Succeeding In School	195
What Is Executive Function?	196
What Type Of Learner Am I?	198
Three-Step Planning	200
Finding Your Motivation	202
Setting Goals	204
Awesome Studying Techniques	206
Conquering Time Management	208
Harness Your Hyperfocus	210

Let's Get Organized   212

CHAPTER 13: PRACTICE SELF-CARE

Practice Self-Care   215

Take A Mini Mental Vacation   218

Create Your Own Sensory Space   219

Hang Out With Your Pets   220

Take A Walk (In Nature If You Can)   221

Tell Yourself Positive Self-Affirmations   222

Tell Yourself Positive Body Image Affirmations   224

Stay Hydrated   226

Eat Healthily   227

Create Your Own Sensory Coping Kit   228

You're Not Alone   229

My Coping Tools   230

Get A Good Night's Sleep   231

CHAPTER 14: MY FUTURE PLANS

Setting Yourself Up For Success   235

My Step Ladder To Success   237

Unlocking Solutions   238

Letter To Your Future Self   239

Who I Am vs. Who I Want To Be   240

Ingredients For Success   242

Using My Toolbox   243

Looking For Silver Linings   244

How To Look For Silver Linings   244

My Future Is Bright   247

Crossing Your Bridge To Happiness   248

Final Thoughts   250

FOREWORD

Siena Castellon is a role model for young girls who think differently.

When I first learned about Siena, I was really impressed by all of her accomplishments in math and physics. At age ten, she went to the Stanford Pre-Collegiate Summer Institute. She then went on to the Summer Program at Cambridge University Perimeter Institute of Theoretical Physics in Canada. With these credentials, she was accepted to one of the best high schools for mathematics in the UK. Unfortunately, both teachers and male students bullied her and told her that girls were not good at physics and math. The school also refused to make simple accommodations to reduce sensory issues from fluorescent lights and noise. Her unfortunate experiences with bullying occurred shortly before this book was published.

Siena's book provides lots of practical advice that I would find really helpful. She uses the same time management tools that I use. Having a calendar where I can see an entire month makes scheduling easier. The section on how to make and keep friends is one of the best chapters. It contains easy-to-understand guidance.

Temple Grandin

Professor of Animal Science
Colorado State University
Author of *Thinking in Pictures* and *The Autistic Brain*

BEAUTY BEGINS THE MOMENT YOU DECIDE TO BE YOURSELF.

- COCO CHANEL

INTRODUCTION

I know how hard it is to find practical autism-focused guidance and advice that is written for autistic girls. I also know what it's like to feel lost, misunderstood, and a sense of overwhelming helplessness. The good news is that it doesn't have to be this way. Over the years, I've created many different ways to compensate and navigate around my autism-related challenges. I'm writing this book because I hope that sharing my coping strategies will help make life a little easier for you.

Being a teenager is hard, but being an autistic teen girl takes it to a stratospheric level. In addition to the usual teenage hardships, we have to deal with debilitating sensory issues, crippling social anxiety, deciphering cryptic social rules, and trying to fit in. Our challenges can feel like insurmountable obstacles and can impact our mental health.

I hope that if you take anything away from this book, it's that there are many strategies that you can use to lighten your load. I also hope that this book helps you to identify your many talents and abilities, and empowers you to capitalize on your many strengths. Schools often only focus on our weaknesses and can make us feel that we're never good enough. Sometimes the best thing you can do is to block out all the negative noise. As long as you know that you tried your best and you believe in yourself, nothing else matters.

Finally, I hope that this book reminds you that you're not alone. Never forget that you're part of a sisterhood of autistic girls who see you and who understand and embrace you for who you are.

We're out here rooting for you!

HOW TO USE THIS BOOK

I have written this book to be a companion and extension of my first book – **The Spectrum Girl's Survival Guide: How To Grow Up Awesome and Autistic**. In this book, I expand on the themes I discussed in **The Spectrum Girl's Survival Guide** by providing practical information, advice, and exercises to help you to overcome some of the many challenges you face. Once again, I've created the type of book I wish I could have benefitted from when I was growing up. A book I could relate to and that provides advice, guidance, and skill-building exercises in the areas that autistic girls struggle with the most.

I have chosen the themes in this book on the feedback I have received from hundreds of autistic girls, parents, teachers, and autism experts. There are chapters on identifying and understanding your emotions and chapters linking your thoughts, feelings, and behaviors. There is a chapter that teaches you to identify and reframe negative thoughts. There are chapters on making and maintaining friendships and on how to deal with bullying. And chapters that focus on succeeding in school, recognizing your talents and strengths, and practicing self-care. Finally, there is a chapter on your future plans because no matter how bleak things may sometimes be, your future is bright and full of endless possibilities.

You can go through this book from beginning to end, or you can skip around, starting wherever makes sense. There is no right or wrong way to use this book. Use this book in the best way that works for you. What works for me may not work for you. The exercises in this toolkit are not intended to be rigid and inflexible. This toolkit should be applied and adjusted to your personal preferences and needs. It's designed to be dynamic and adaptive, especially since you'll need different coping skills and strategies for different situations.

Don't be afraid to use your own creativity, ingenuity and problem-solving abilities to modify or create coping strategies that work for you.

I hope that this book helps you recognize that you're the captain of your ship and that your challenges do not have to hold you back.

BELIEVE IN YOURSELF AND YOUR AWESOMENESS.

KNOW THAT THE STRENGTH INSIDE YOU IS GREATER THAN ANY OBSTACLE.

ALWAYS END THE DAY WITH A POSITIVE THOUGHT.

Chapter 1

UNDERSTANDING YOUR EMOTIONS

Decoding Your Emotions

Emotions are at the root of most of our thoughts and actions. Many of us avoid dealing with our emotions. Or, we act on our emotions without understanding the underlying reason for these actions. Identifying the emotion you're feeling, and the cause of this feeling can explain why you act the way you do. Our thoughts, emotions, and physical reactions are interconnected. Learning to understand our emotions gives us more control over our feelings, thoughts, and physical reactions. This insight allows us to recognize and alter any behavior that may be negatively affecting our lives.

Identifying our emotions isn't about solving or numbing these emotions, sometimes recognizing them for what they are is all you have to do. Recognizing your feelings will allow you to take care of yourself when you feel upset or distressed. For example, if you're feeling angry, instead of suppressing your anger, try doing a physical activity, such as going for a walk. Redirecting your emotion into a healthy activity will make you feel better.

Since our body also expresses our emotions, when we can identify the physical reaction and where it's located, we can learn how to cope with the physical response and the emotion before these feelings and thoughts fester and begin to affect your mental health and wellbeing. If you take the time to decode your feelings, you'll learn that your body sends you lots of messages. As you become more skilled in identifying a particular feeling's physical location, you'll be able to connect which emotion is often associated with which sensation.

In this chapter, we'll focus on helping you to develop the skills that'll allow you to identify, label, and express your emotions. We'll also focus on giving you the tools you need to apply the vocabulary of emotions to your personal experiences.

What Is Alexithymia?

Do you struggle to identify and talk about the emotions that you are feeling? You're not alone. It's very common for autistic people to struggle with identifying, describing, and processing their emotions. This difficulty is called **alexithymia** (which literally means having no words for emotions).

Alexithymia is characterized by three main difficulties:

1. Difficulties identifying what you're feeling

2. Difficulties describing your feelings to others

3. Difficulties distinguishing between your emotions and the physical sensations related to an emotional response, such as a rapid heartbeat.

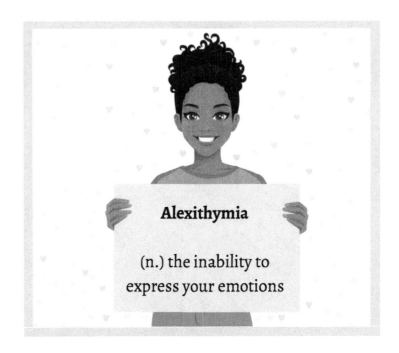

Alexithymia

(n.) the inability to express your emotions

Wheel of Emotions

The wheel of emotions set out below categorizes our emotions into six main categories: love, joy, surprise, sadness, anger, and fear. Within each of these six emotions are two sub-categories that are a variation of this emotion. As you do some of the activities in this book, you may want to refer back to this wheel.

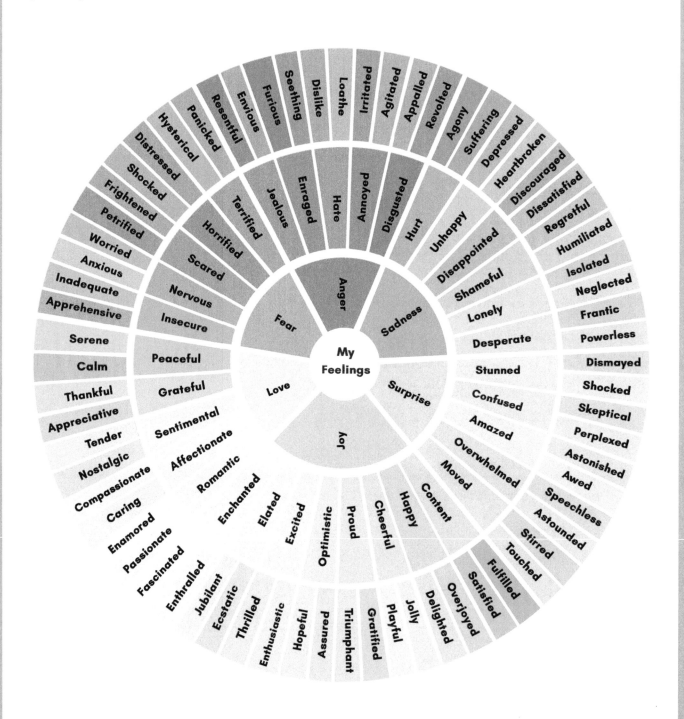

Feelings Vocabulary

Set a timer for 5 minutes and write down as many words that describe your feelings. Don't worry about spelling or making a mistake. Use whatever words or phrases that come to mind that describe different feelings. Stop when the timer goes off. If you get stuck, use the wheel of emotions on the previous page.

Name That Feeling

Using the list of words and phrases that you wrote on the wall, sort your list of feelings into general categories in the table below.

Happy:

Sad:

Angry:

Scared:

Proud:

Nervous

Excited:

Cheerful:

Other:

Other:

My Body's Response To My Feelings

Sometimes, we don't realize that we feel certain emotions in specific parts of our bodies. For example, when you are nervous your hands may sweat and tremble. Learning to decode our bodies' language is a useful skill because our body gives us clues as to how we are feeling. These clues can be especially useful in situations where you are uncertain about what you are feeling or cannot verbally express your feelings. This exercise will help you to start to recognize your body's response to your feelings.

On the two silhouettes on the following page, indicate where in your body, you feel each of the following emotions:

- Happy

- Sad

- Angry

- Scared

- Surprised

- Lonely

When I'm feeling stressed I get a headache.

What other emotions can your body feel?

_____

_____

_____

Add these other emotions to the silhouettes on the following page.

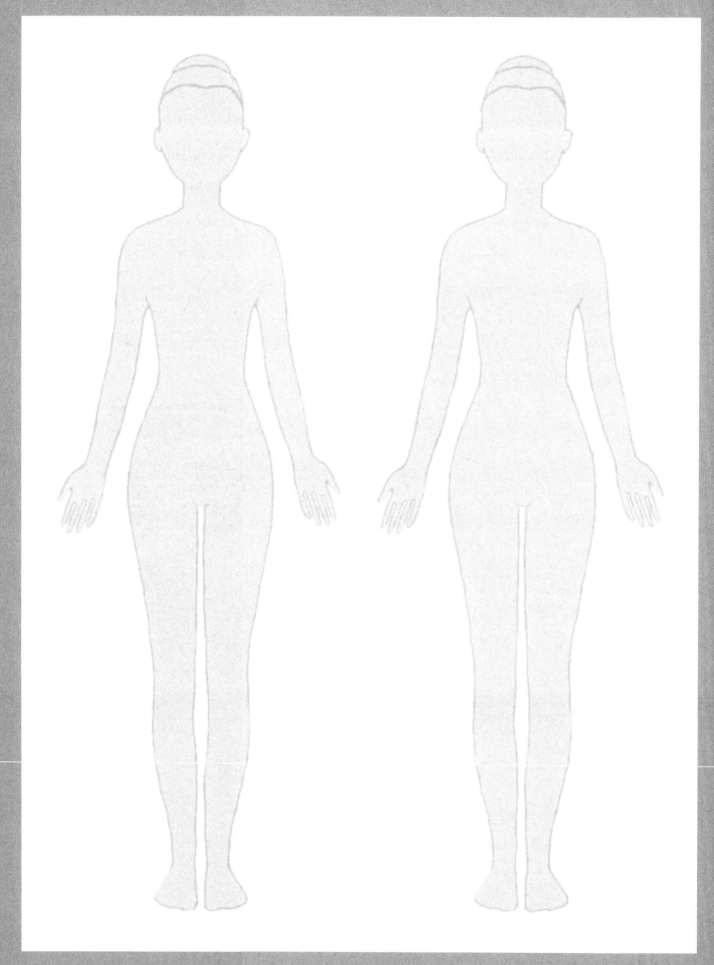

My Emotion Thermometer

Feelings are experienced at different levels of intensity. I find that one useful way to measure the intensity of a particular feeling is to use a thermometer. Select a feeling (happy, sad, angry, scared, or any other emotion). Next, think of words that describe how that emotion feels at the following four intensities:

- 25% intensity

- 50% intensity

- 75% intensity

- 100% intensity

For example, if you choose happy, 25% may be "hopeful," 50% may be "cheerful," 75% may be "excited," and 100% may be "elated." It you find the Wheel of Emotions on page 3 helpful feel free to use it.

For each of these four intensities, pay particular attention to how you physically experience the emotion in your body. Does your heart rate increase? Do you feel jittery, fidgety or apprehensive?

Once you're able to assign an intensity to your feeling, you'll be in a better position to determine how you're feeling.

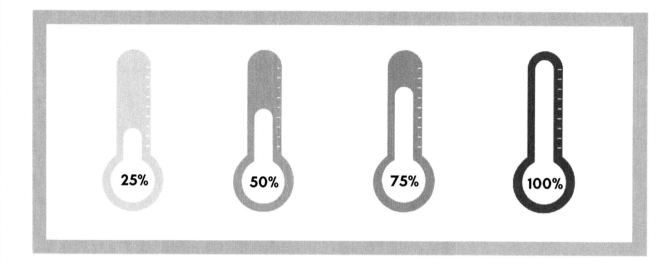

Emotion: _____

At 25% I feel: _____

My body cues are: _____

At 50% I feel: _____

My body cues are: _____

At 75% I feel: _____

My body cues are: _____

At 100% I feel: _____

My body cues are: _____

Linking My Feelings, Thoughts, and Behaviors

Connecting your emotions, thoughts, and behaviors is a useful tool for understanding and dealing with your feelings, especially your negative emotions. Below is a diagram that will help you to determine how feelings, thoughts and behaviors are different, yet interconnected.

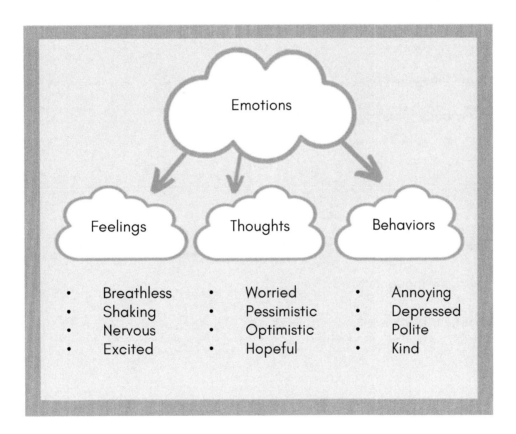

People's emotions are unique to them. We all react in different ways to our experiences. What makes you happy or sad may not be the same for someone else. For example, solving complicated math problems makes me happy. Whereas doing math problems in your spare time may be your worst nightmare!

The activity on the next page will help you to link your feelings, thoughts, and behaviors.

Happy

I'm happy when _____

When I'm happy, my thoughts are _____

When I'm happy, my body feels _____

Sad

I'm sad when _____

When I'm sad, my thoughts are _____

When I'm sad, my body feels _____

Relaxed

I'm relaxed when _____

When I'm relaxed, my thoughts are _____

When I'm relaxed, my body feels _____

Angry

I'm angry when _____

When I'm angry, my thoughts are _____

When I'm angry, my body feels _____

Excited

I'm excited when _____

When I'm excited, my thoughts are _____

When I'm excited, my body feels _____

Lonely

I'm lonely when _____

When I'm lonely, my thoughts are _____

When I'm lonely, my body feels _____

Getting to Know My Feelings

Complete the sentences below with the first thing that comes to mind.

I feel happy when

I feel loved when

I feel angry when

I feel helpless when

I feel sorry when

I feel proud when

I feel strong when

I feel sad when

I feel scared when

I feel excited when

I feel jealous when

I feel embarrassed when

I feel annoyed when

I feel hurt when

I AM IN CHARGE OF HOW I FEEL AND TODAY I CHOOSE HAPPINESS.

Chapter 2

EXPRESSING AND CONTROLLING YOUR EMOTIONS

● ●

Knowing My Triggers

Sometimes a feeling can take you by surprise because it appears to come out of nowhere. However, this is rarely the case. By paying close attention to what is happening immediately before we get overwhelmed by an emotion, we can discover the trigger that caused us to feel this emotion. **Triggers** are events, situations, people, or experiences that cause us to feel a specific emotion. We often associate triggers with negative experiences, but triggers can also set off positive emotions. For example, the smell of watermelon makes me think of warm summer days.

For each of the feelings set out on the next page, list at least two situations that trigger that emotion. For example, playing with your dog or swimming in the sea may trigger happiness, whereas being bullied or not being invited to a party might trigger sadness. To identify your triggers for each feeling, ask yourself these questions:

- Who makes me feel this way?

- Where do I feel this way?

- What am I thinking about when I have this feeling?

- What events, situations, or experiences make me feel this way?

Happy

Trigger: _____

Trigger: _____

Sad

Trigger: _____

Trigger: _____

Relaxed

Trigger: _____

Trigger: _____

Angry

Trigger: _____

Trigger: _____

Excited

Trigger: _____

Trigger: _____

Lonely

Trigger: _____

Trigger: _____

What Pushes Your Buttons?

The first step in learning to manage your triggers is to identify them. Below are some things that may trigger you.

What Pushes Your Buttons?

- [ ] Being touched
- [ ] Loud noises
- [ ] Feeling embarassed
- [ ] Being tired
- [ ] Being hungry
- [ ] Being criticized
- [ ] Being treated unfairly
- [ ] Being interrupted

- [ ] Being ignored
- [ ] Being bumped into
- [ ] Being left out
- [ ] Being disrespected
- [ ] Being mistreated
- [ ] Being yelled at
- [ ] Being told what to do
- [ ] Being bullied

Connecting the Dots

Being aware of the triggers that cause you to feel certain emotions is an essential tool that will allow you to manage your emotions. Recognizing your triggers is a skill that you can develop and perfect with practice. Once you can identify your triggers, you'll be able to find ways to manage these triggers and, will be in a better position to control your feelings.

For each of the following emotions, write down three situations, people, places, or other triggers that make you feel this way.

Happy

1

2

3

Sad

1

2

3

Relaxed

1 _____
2 _____
3 _____

Angry

1 _____
2 _____
3 _____

Excited

1 _____
2 _____
3 _____

Lonely

1 _____
2 _____
3 _____

Trigger Tracking

This week, pay attention to your feelings and what is happening immediately before or while you feel this emotion. At the end of each day, write down one emotion and the trigger that caused this feeling. Don't forget to include positive triggers too.

Monday

Emotion:

Trigger:

Tuesday

Emotion:

Trigger:

Wednesday

Emotion:

Trigger:

Thursday

Emotion:

Trigger:

Friday

Emotion:

Trigger:

Use Your Sensory Powers

When you get overwhelmed by a situation, it may feel like you can't regulate or control your emotions. The good news is that you can use your senses to help you self-regulate. For example, when I'm stressed I like to listen to music (sound) while stroking my dog (touch) in my lavender-scented room (smell). Doing activities that engage my senses helps to calm me.

In this activity, you will create a toolkit of sensory items that you find comforting, soothing, calming, or that make you feel good. Since what works for me may not work for you, this strategy will work best if you tailor this activity for the type of sensory input that works best for you. The following list includes some ideas to get you started, but don't limit yourself to this list. Use your creativity to come up with additional sensory experiences that will help you manage your emotions.

Sight – For example, looking at:

- Photographs of good moments with friends or loved ones
- Images of cute animals
- TikTok videos
- Lava lamps
- Images of nature

Sound – For example, listening to:

- Music, including classical music
- Ocean waves
- Rain or a waterfall
- Birds chirping
- A gentle breeze

Taste - For example, eating:

- A warm, creamy hot chocolate
- Salted popcorn
- Chocolate
- Olives
- Ginger
- A sour lemon

Smell - For example, smelling:

- Lavender
- Pineapple
- Coconut
- Cinnamon
- Pine cones
- Freshly baked cookies

Touch - For example:

- Hugging a soft pillow
- Holding something fluffy
- Squeezing a stress ball
- Lying under a weighted blanket
- Stroking a pet
- Playing with slime

When I feel overwhelmed I like to bake. It's a soothing activity that allows me to use all my senses.

Fill in the table below with sensory experiences that will help to comfort and soothe you. Next time you feel overwhelmed by your emotions, you'll be able to self-regulate by using your tailor-made sensory toolkit.

Sight:

Sound:

Taste:

Smell:

Touch:

My Soundtrack

Music has the power to influence our mood. It's also an outlet through which we can express how we're feeling. Did you know that we usually listen to music that matches our mood?

When I'm in a bad mood, I will listen to somber music (Lana Del Rey). Whereas when I'm in a good mood, I'll listen to upbeat music (Taylor Swift).

What type of music or which songs do you listen to when you're happy? Or when you're sad?

_____

_____

_____

_____

_____

GOOD MUSIC CALMS MY SOUL. IT TAKES ME TO ANOTHER PLACE, AWAY FROM MY PROBLEMS.

Since music has the power to change the way we feel, we can use music as a tool to help us control how we are feeling. For each of the following feelings, list a song that you associate with that feeling. The song you pick can be a song that makes you feel that emotion. It can also be a song that describes the way you express that emotion, or a song that you like to listen to when you want to get into a particular mood. As you do this activity, you may find it helpful to listen to each song as you list it.

Happy: _____

Sad: _____

Relaxed: _____

Angry: _____

Excited: _____

Lonely: _____

Unleash Your Imagination

Have you ever used your imagination to escape or to cope with a stressful situation? If so, you were using "guided imagery." **Guided imagery** is a powerful tool that you can use to control your emotions and to help you feel calm in stressful situations. Guided imagery is a great calming strategy for autistic individuals because it involves using all of your senses to visualize an image of a person, place, or time that makes you feel safe, relaxed, peaceful, and happy. Since most autistic people have heightened senses, this technique is particularly well suited to us.

Think of a place that you associate with feeling safe and calm. It could be your grandparent's house, the time your hiked through the woods or enjoyed a picnic at your local park. If you're having trouble, here are some suggestions:

- Imagine yourself relaxing on a sunny tropical beach. Listen to the gentle swishing of the waves. Swimming in the warm, soothing sea. Dig your toes into the soft, powdery sand.

- Picture yourself curled up on a comfy, over-sized armchair relaxing in front of a roaring fire with a warm cup of hot cocoa in a remote, cozy, wood cabin, surrounded by towering mountains and glistening snow.

- Visualize yourself sitting by a gentle, soothing waterfall deep in the heart of the Amazon rainforest. Feel the soft mist against your face. Listen to the tropical birds chirping.

Have you ever used your imagination to escape or to cope with a stressful situation? If so, It's important to remember that this strategy relies on using all your senses. For example, don't just imagine yourself in a remote mountain cabin. In your imagination, look around you. Hear the crackling wood. Feel the fire's warmth against your skin. Inhale the musky, earthy scent of the burning wood. Touch the fluffy blanket. Taste the sweetness of the hot chocolate sprinkled with marshmallows. Look out of the window at the pine trees laden with glistening snow. Experience the feeling of being warm and safe.

Your goal is to immerse yourself fully in the scene. This includes what you can see, hear, taste, smell and touch, as well as how you feel. The more details you add to your imagery, the more useful this technique will be in helping you to control your emotions

Color-Coding My Feelings

Did you know there's a field of psychology that focuses on the affect that color has on our emotions and state of mind? Your surroundings influence the way you feel. Have you ever noticed that certain places are especially stressful or irritating? Or that certain places make you feel calm and relaxed? There's a good chance that the colors in those spaces play a part in determining your mood.

Studies have shown that when some people look at the color red, their heart rate increases. These studies also found that warm colors - reds, yellows, and oranges - can evoke various emotions ranging from comfort and warmth to hostility and anger. On the other hand, cool colors - greens, blues, and purples - often evoke feelings of calmness, as well as sadness.

Marketing and advertising companies rely on color psychology to influence how we feel about their products and to encourage us to buy them. For example, they use color in their marketing campaigns to make us hungry, to encourage trust, evoke feelings of calmness and joy, and in countless other ways.

Color psychology can also be applied to our everyday lives. Need to be creative? Try using purple. Purple is made up of red and blue, which is the perfect balance between stimulation and serenity. Light purple is an ideal color for creating a peaceful and serene environment, which is why I've used a lot of purple in this book. If you want to create a calming atmosphere, consider using green or blue.

Becoming more aware of how specific colors influence your mood will give you the tools to use the psychology of color to manage your feelings.

For this activity, you will need different-colored pens, crayons, or pencils. For each emotion on the following pink notes, select a color that reminds you of that feeling and add that color onto the relevant note. Be as expressive and creative as you want.

Happy

Sad

Relaxed

Angry

Excited

Lonely

Practice Gratitude

Have you ever found yourself dwelling on an insult or fixating on your mistakes? Criticisms often have a greater impact than compliments, and bad news frequently draws more attention than good. If we only pay attention to the negative, that is where our focus will be. What if it didn't have to be this way? Practicing gratitude can rewire your brain, so you're more likely to focus on the many positives in your life.

Gratitude is an emotion we feel when we recognize and appreciate the good things in our life. When you shift your focus to the positive and are intentional about practicing gratitude, your emotional wellbeing, and happiness increase. Practicing gratitude can help you become more optimistic, hopeful, empathic, and appreciative about what you have. In other words, it opens your eyes to the fact that what you have is truly enough.

Below are some ideas on how you can practice gratitude in your daily life:

Focus On The Positive. Although it may be more natural to fixate on the negative, such as the hurtful comments, or the things that go wrong, focusing on the positive can have a much bigger impact on your live. When you focus on the positive, you start to feel better. Next time something doesn't go the way you would have liked, instead of obsessing on what went wrong, intentionally think about what is going right. You can start small. Think about the good things in your life or even the good that happened during the day. Allow yourself to smile about it and let your thoughts focus on this feeling. Noticing the good and focusing on it can help you feel the positive emotions all over again.

Feel Your Feelings. Spending time feeling your emotions can help you focus on your feelings of gratefulness. Although not all of your feelings will be positive, when you allow yourself to feel them, your positive feelings will be amplified. When you're aware of your feelings and are actively feeling them, you can experience greater joy. The more you focus on gratitude and the feelings associated with it, the more grateful you'll feel.

Share Your Gratitude. Share your feelings of gratitude with others. Let your family and friends know that you're grateful for them and why. Point out the positive qualities that you notice in others. Be generous with your compliments. By switching your focus to your blessings, you'll notice the good more and more frequently. When you share what you are grateful for, you will help others, and yourself feel more optimistic.

Keep A Gratitude Journal. Keeping a gratitude journal can be a great way to focus on what you are grateful for. Writing down what you are thankful for helps reinforce positive feelings. If you do this before going to bed, you may sleep better. Regularly reading your journal will help you to recognize and appreciate the many good things in your life that you may have been overlooking or may have been taking for granted.

NEVER LET THE THINGS YOU WANT MAKE YOU FORGET THE THINGS YOU HAVE.

Random Acts Of Kindness

Being kind not only benefits others, it also greatly benefits you by making you feel good about your actions and yourself. Here are a few ideas.

- Keep a daily gratitude journal.
- Tell someone you love them and why.
- Open a door for someone.
- Spend 10 minutes picking up trash.
- Do something kind for a homeless person.
- Compliment a stranger.
- Pack up a donation bag.
- Do something nice for someone who is sick.
- Give three people on social media compliments.
- Do something nice for yourself.
- Take an entire day off social media.
- Spend an afternoon outdoors.
- Do something kind for a neighbor.
- Sign up to volunteer somewhere.
- Donate gently used books.
- Make everyone's bed.
- Do something nice for a sibling or parent.
- Compliment a friend or loved one.
- Recycle bottles.
- Bake cookies for someone.
- Encourage someone.
- Clean your room without being asked.
- Ask a senior adult about their past.

- Donate food to a food drive.

- Be thankful when you learn something new.

- Focus on your strengths.

- Ask yourself what you can learn from your failures.

- Steer clear of gossip.

- Share your umbrella with someone.

- Be friendly to a new student.

- Do something nice for a friend.

- Leave a positive note in a library book.

- Watch inspiring videos that make you feel good about the world.

- Seize the opportunity to learn from a difficult situation.

- Text someone good morning or good night.

- Start a piggy bank for a cause.

I'm taking the entire day off social media.

I'm going to leave a positive note on a stranger's car windshield.

I'm keeping a gratitude journal that I write in every evening.

I'm doing something kind for my younger sister.

JUST BECAUSE I CAN'T EXPLAIN THE FEELINGS CAUSING MY ANXIETY, DOESN'T MAKE THEM LESS VALID.

Chapter 3

UNDERSTANDING YOUR ANXIETY

What Is Anxiety?

Anxiety is a normal emotion that we feel when we're nervous, worried, and afraid. It's the feeling you get when you have a worry that you can't stop thinking about, one that starts to take over your thoughts. You may feel anxious that something unpleasant that happened in the past will happen again or that something terrible will happen to you in the future. For example, you could be worried about embarrassing yourself by saying the wrong thing, nervous about a change in your routine, or scared about being bullied.

It's normal to feel anxious during your teen years. It's a time in our lives when a lot is happening. We're becoming more independent, our bodies and brains are changing, and we're facing new experiences, opportunities, and challenges. You may find yourself worrying about starting high school, looking a particular way, fitting in with friends, or doing well on exams.

Anxiety can be a beneficial emotion in that it can help keep you safe by alerting you and forcing you to focus on the situation. It can also help to prepare you for a stressful situation, such as if you have to give a presentation in front of your class. Unfortunately, sometimes anxiety can stick around when it isn't needed or wanted, which can make life really challenging.

For most teens, anxiety doesn't last very long and goes away on its own. But for some teens, it doesn't go away or is so intense that it stops them from being able to do everyday things and from living their lives in the way they would like. If you're one of these teens, I hope I can help by sharing the strategies, exercises and activities that I use to manage my anxiety and that may help to reduce your anxiety too.

The Symptoms of Anxiety

When we face stressful situations, it can set off our brain's in-built fire alarm, which serves as a warning signal to alert us that something isn't right and that we need to deal with it. Once the warning signal is triggered, you'll start to feel a range of different physical sensations. These sensations can include:

- A fast heartbeat or an irregular heartbeat.

- Breathing very fast (hyperventilating).

- Shortness of breath or chest pain.

- Feeling dizzy or light-headed.

- Loss of appetite.

- Feeling nervous, on edge, or panicky.

- A dry mouth.

- Pins and needles.

- Feeling overwhelmed, or full of dread.

- Feeling nauseous, or having stomach cramps.

- Avoiding situations and events that make you uncomfortable.

- Finding it difficult to concentrate.

- Suffering from frequent headaches.

- Difficulties sleeping and restlessness.

- Persistent feelings of impending doom.

- Feeling like your legs are wobbly or weak.

Our brain wants the situation to go away, so it makes us feel more alert, stops us thinking about other things, and even pumps more blood to our legs to help us run away.

One of the most frustrating things about having anxiety is knowing as you're panicking that there's no reason to panic, but being unable to shut off the emotion.

Exploring Your Anxiety

The best way to manage your anxiety is to get a better understanding of the specific concerns and situations that cause you stress. By recognizing and identifying what causes you anxiety, you'll be able to find creative ways to manage these feelings. Some situations, such as your first day at a new school, will be obvious. But other situations will be more subtle. For example, the fear of having a sensory overload at school or of being bullied may be causing you anxiety.

On the pink notes notes below and on the following page, list the concerns, circumstances, or thoughts that make you anxious or nervous.

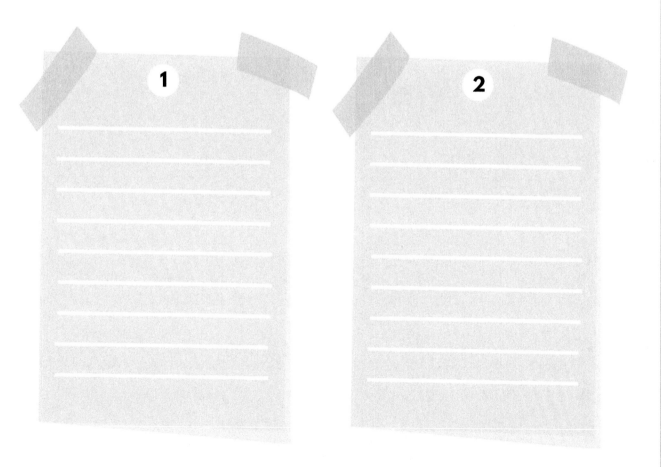

Now go back and rate each one. Use #1 for the situation that causes you the most anxiety, and #6 for the situation you find the easiest to manage.

Next, pick a situation that you labeled as #1 or #2 (one of your hardest, most anxiety-provoking situations), and answer the following questions with that particular situation in mind.

What are some of the thoughts or concerns you have about this situation?

Your answer may include concerns like:

- I'm going to make a fool of myself.

- It's too overwhelming.

- I'm going to fail.

- I'm not going to be able to do it.

- I'm going to get rejected.

_____

_____

_____

_____

_____

_____

Now consider <u>all</u> of the situations you listed that cause you anxiety and any other situations you can think of.

How do you respond when you are feeling anxious in these situations? What actions do you usually take?

_____

_____

_____

Think about the ways that your anxiety has affected your life. Are there activities that you wish you could take part in? Are there places where you'd like to go? Describe three ways in which your anxiety impacts you or holds you back from living your best life.

1 _____

_____

2 _____

_____

3 _____

_____

Imagine that you wake up tomorrow to discover that all your anxiety has suddenly gone. How would your life change?

_____

_____

_____

_____

What are some actions you can take to reduce or manage your anxiety?

_____

_____

_____

_____

Identify a few people who can support you in starting to take control of your anxiety. They can be friends, family members, teachers, and close friends.

_____

_____

_____

Balancing Your Worries

Almost every situation has pros (benefits) and cons (drawbacks) that can influence your decisions. When determining what action to take, weigh the pros and cons so you can make an informed decision. Write down a situation that is causing you to worry. For example, if you're worried about joining the school choir, your pros could be that you could make new friends and enjoy performing at school events. Your cons could be that you may struggle to make new friends and that joining the choir will take up a lot of your free time.

Below, write down your action plan to help you overcome your worry. Include the coping skills you will use to overcome your worry. For example, for the choir example mentioned above, you could resolve to practice your singing and learn some of the words to the songs so that you feel more confident and prepared about joining the school choir.

My Worries and Pros and Cons Balancing Action Plan

AT ANY GIVEN POINT YOU HAVE THE POWER TO SAY "THIS IS NOT HOW MY STORY IS GOING TO END."

What's The Worst That Could Happen?

Whenever you find yourself getting anxious about something that may happen in the future, ask yourself: "What's the worst that could happen?" By asking yourself this question, you're looking at the problem from a different perspective. When we face our fears, we dilute them, and we take away their power. More often than not, our worst case scenario is less frightening than the debilitating anticipatory anxiety we feel about the unknown.

Worrying is also a waste of time because the chances are that our fear will not come to pass. But even if our fear did happen, in most situations, the worst possible outcome isn't as bad as we feared. Most of the time, it will be something we can live with, even if it's unpleasant or embarrassing. I've had some really cringeworthy moments that I was mortified by. Although I was upset at the time, I now look back on those moments with a sense of humor and laugh. Some day, when you're more distanced from the situation, you may even look back on your embarrassing moments and find them amusing too.

Next time you find yourself worrying about a future event, ask yourself the following questions:

- What's the worst that can happen?

- If the worst thing happens, what will be the consequence?

- How have I coped in the past? What can I do to cope better this time?

- What is realistically more likely to happen?

- Is wasting your time and energy on worrying productive or helpful?

Anxiety Fact Checking

Since worries are thoughts that lead to anxious feelings, one way to manage your anxiety is to challenge your worry-related thoughts. Use the following questions to try out this anxiety management strategy.

What are you worried about?

_____

_____

What evidence do you have that this worry will come true?

_____

_____

What's the absolute worst that could happen if it did come true?

_____

_____

What's most likely to happen if your worry does come true?

_____

_____

What's the likelihood that you'll be okay (in a day, a week, a month, or a year)?

_____

_____

_____

_____

Tracking My Anxiety Triggers

Over the next week, pay close attention to your feelings and what is causing you to feel anxious. At the end of each day, write down one anxiety trigger, and rate the intensity level of your anxiety on a scale of 1 – 10 by circling the relevant number. A #1 is not at all anxious, and a #10 is the highest possible level of anxiety.

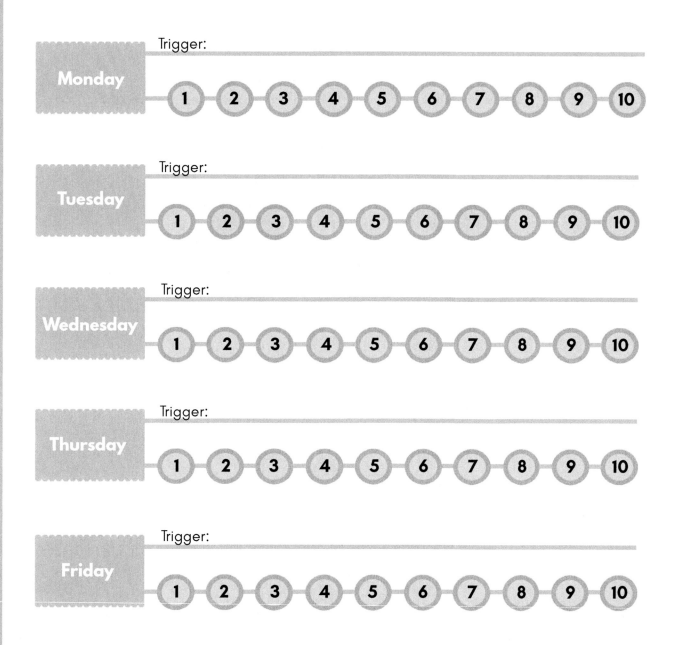

Monday

Trigger:

1 2 3 4 5 6 7 8 9 10

Tuesday

Trigger:

1 2 3 4 5 6 7 8 9 10

Wednesday

Trigger:

1 2 3 4 5 6 7 8 9 10

Thursday

Trigger:

1 2 3 4 5 6 7 8 9 10

Friday

Trigger:

1 2 3 4 5 6 7 8 9 10

My Anxiety Thermometer

Let's use the thermometer again, except this time, we'll use it to measure the intensity of your anxiety levels. As you think about your anxiety, think of words to describe how your anxiety feels at 25%, 50%, 75%, and 100%. For example, 25% is a little unpleasant, 50% is hard but tolerable, 75% is very uncomfortable, and 100% is intolerable. For each of these intensities, pay particular attention to how your body experiences anxiety.

Does your heart rate increase? Do you feel faint? Does your mouth get dry?

Once you have answered the questions on the next page, you can refer back to your answers to help you identify your anxiety levels.

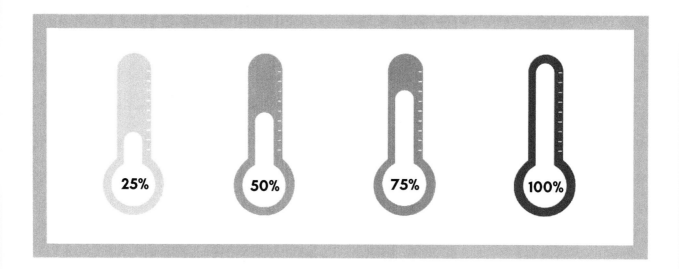

My Anxiety Levels

At 25% I feel: _____

My cues are: _____

At 50% I feel: _____

My body cues are: _____

At 75% I feel: _____

My body cues are: _____

At 100% I feel: _____

My body cues are: _____

Healthy Coping Activities

The next time you feel anxious, try doing some of the healthy coping activities set out in the following list:

- Plan something to look forward to.
- Look at photos of happy memories.
- Create a happy playlist.
- Blow bubbles.
- Read inspirational quotes.
- Compliment yourself.
- Look at cute animal pictures.
- Do something you love.
- Go for a walk outside.
- Watch the clouds.
- Jump rope.
- Paint your nails.
- Sing and dance.
- Have a picnic.
- Bake a cake.
- Organize your closet.
- Play a board game.
- Tie-dye a shirt.
- Ride a bike.
- Walk a dog.
- Play a video game.
- Try a new recipe.
- Read your favorite book.

- Listen to music.

- Do origami.

- Write a poem.

- Think of something happy.

- Do something kind.

- Build something.

- Play an instrument.

- Watch a feel-good movie.

- Take a long bath.

- Jump on a trampoline.

- Do a puzzle.

- Smile and laugh.

- Weave, knit, or crochet.

- Make art.

- Clean, declutter or organize.

- Use aromatherapy.

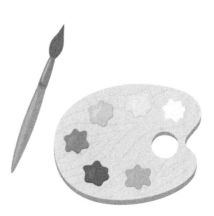

- Look around for something beautiful.

- Remember a time when you were successful.

- Think of a funny memory.

- Make a list of five good things in your life.

- Do something nice for someone.

- Play a card game.

- Say something kind to yourself.

- Use a relaxation app.

- Schedule time for yourself.

- Make a list for the future.

- Identify a positive thought.

I WISH PEOPLE KNEW THAT SOME OF US HAVE TO USE A TREMENDOUS AMOUNT OF ENERGY SO WE CAN APPEAR TO BE LIKE EVERYONE ELSE.

Chapter 4

UNDERSTANDING YOUR SOCIAL ANXIETY

The Symptoms of Social Anxiety

Social anxiety is the fear of social situations that involve interaction with other people. At its core, it's a fear of being embarrassed, appearing foolish, or being rejected, criticized or laughed at. Although social anxiety is very common, it's especially prevalent in people who are autistic. People with social anxiety tend to feel self-conscious and uncomfortable about being noticed or judged by others. We're often perceived as shy, quiet, withdrawn, unfriendly, and disinterested. Before I was diagnosed with social anxiety, I was known as the shy, unfriendly, quiet girl. If you have social anxiety, you may have been perceived this way too. However, social anxiety is much more than shyness.

Societal anxiety is an intense fear of social interaction that doesn't go away. It affects our relationships, ability to participate in everyday activities, and our school life. In other words, social anxiety can wreak havoc on every aspect of our lives. Although we recognize that some of our fears may be irrational or unreasonable, we are often powerless to overcome them. The most frustrating thing about having social anxiety is that it prevents us from doing things that we really want to do. For example, many of us want to make friends, spend time having fun with our friends, and to be involved and engaged in our school community, but our social anxiety often stops us from being able to.

You may have social anxiety if you:

- Dread everyday activities, such as going to school.

- Avoid social situations, such as parties and weddings.

- Have anticipatory anxiety; a debilitating fear of social situations before and leading up to an event.

- Have a fear of being judged negatively, especially socially.

- Always worry about saying or doing something that will make you look foolish.

- Worry that others will notice your social discomfort.

- Avoid expressing your opinions or initiating conversations because you are afraid of being dismissed or saying the wrong thing.

- Stay quiet or blend into the background to avoid drawing any attention to yourself.

- Judge yourself harshly following conversations, or other interactions with people.

- Prepare scripts in advance of social interactions to make conversations easier.

- Avoid speaking on the phone.

- Find it difficult to do things when others are watching you, such as eating in front of others.

- Worry that you may blush.

- Have frequent panic attacks, or are overwhelmed by a sense of fear and dread.

Exploring Your Social Anxiety

Since autism affects our social and communication skills, it's very common for autistic individuals to develop social anxiety. My social anxiety can be traced to my epic failures in understanding social interactions and a lifetime of feeling different and out of sync with the rest of the world. Walking on eggshells and always wondering if you said or did the right thing is very stressful.

Did I say something offensive?

Did I talk too much?

Did I talk enough?

Did I ask the right questions?

Did I vary the tone of my voice?

Did I change my facial expressions?

These are worries and preoccupations that most people don't have to think about because social skills come naturally to them. But if you're autistic, you have to put a lot more time and effort into your social interactions. If you're like me, you may even plan your social interactions in advance by creating and memorizing scripts. Yet, no matter how much we study and prepare for future conversations and social interactions, they rarely happen exactly as we planned.

During your teen years, social skills become much more complicated, subtle, and difficult to decipher. You may feel social pressure to mimic other people's behavior and interests to keep up, blend in, and avoid bringing unwanted attention to yourself. **Masking** is a common technique that autistic people use to pretend to be like everyone else so that they can be liked and accepted by others. Although masking can work as a short-term strategy, hiding your true self, and keeping up the pretense of being someone that you're not, can eventually lead to social anxiety and other mental health issues.

On the notes below, list the social-related concerns, circumstances, or thoughts that make you anxious or nervous. For example, you may be worried about telling someone that you're autistic because you don't know how they will react or you may dislike meeting new people because you're afraid that you won't know what to say.

1

2

Now go back and rate each one. Use #1 for the situation that causes you the most social anxiety, and #6 for the social situation you find the easiest to manage.

Next, pick a situation that you labeled as #1 or #2 (one of your hardest, most anxiety-provoking situations), and answer the following questions with that particular situation in mind.

What are some of the thoughts or concerns you have about this situation?

Your answer may include concerns like:

- I'm scared of being bullied.

- I'm worried about being laughed at.

- I'm worried I may say something that offends someone.

- What if I don't know what to talk about?

- What if people judge me?

- What if I my sensory issues become too overwhelming?

Now consider <u>all</u> of the situations you listed that cause you social anxiety and any other situations you can think of.

How do you respond when you are feeling anxious in these situations? What actions do you usually take?

_____

_____

_____

Think about the ways that your social anxiety has affected your life. Are there social activities that you wish you could take part in? Are there parties, concerts or other social gatherings you'd love to attend? Describe three ways in which your social anxiety impacts you or holds you back from living your best life.

1 _____

_____

2 _____

_____

3 _____

_____

Imagine that you wake up tomorrow to discover that all your social anxiety has suddenly gone. How would your life change?

_____

_____

_____

_____

What are some steps you can take to control and reduce your social anxiety?

_____

_____

_____

_____

Identify a few people who can support you in taking control of your social anxiety. They could be friends, family members, teachers, and close friends.

_____

_____

_____

_____

The Physical Symptoms of Social Anxiety

Our body reacts in different ways when we experience social anxiety. Below are some of the most common physical symptoms of social anxiety.

Physical symptoms of social anxiety can include:

- An increased heart rate.

- Sweaty palms, or sweating more than usual.

- Shortness of breath.

- Feeling dizzy or faint.

- Feeling shaky or jittery.

- Chest tightness or a choking sensation.

- Having trouble sleeping.

- Awkward, stumbling speech.

- Muscle tension, especially in the jaw and neck.

- Difficulty focusing or concentrating.

- Feeling nauseous.

Common Social Anxiety Triggers

People with social anxiety usually experience significant distress in the following situations.

Social Anxiety Triggers

- Meeting new people.
- Making small talk.
- Attending parties or other social gatherings.
- Being the center of attention.
- Using public restrooms.
- Eating or drinking in public.
- Going to school.
- Being called on in class.
- Participating in class.
- Phone conversations.
- Being watched while doing something.
- Being teased or criticized.
- Stating their opinions.
- Ordering food at a restaurant.
- Returning an item to a store.
- Speaking to unfamiliar people over the phone.

How Social Anxiety Can Affect Your Life

Social anxiety can make our world so much smaller. It can leave us feeling isolated and alone, and it can make us feel like we're watching the world pass us by. When I was being bullied, my social anxiety became so bad that there were days I was unable to go to school, or to even leave the house. It was frustrating, because I wanted to be like other teenagers. I felt pressure to have the typical teenage social life that is depicted in the TV shows, and glossy magazines, but the reality is that my social anxiety made this impossible. You may sometimes feel this way too.

Some of the ways social anxiety could affect your life, include:

- **Feeling lonely or disappointed over missed opportunities for friendship, and fun.** Social anxiety may prevent you from chatting with friends in the lunchroom, joining an after-school club, or going to a concert.

- **Not getting the most out of school.** Social anxiety may keep you from volunteering an participating in class. You may even feel too nervous to ask a question in class, or to ask a teacher for help. You may prefer to blend into the background to avoid bringing any attention to yourself.

- **Missing opportunities to share your talents and explore new interests.** Social anxiety may prevent you from auditioning for the school play, being in the talent show, trying out for a team, or going on a school trip. It can prevent you from developing your strengths and from taking part in activities that you really enjoy.

Redirect Your Focus

When we're in a social situation that makes us nervous, many of us tend to get caught up in our anxious thoughts and feelings. You may be convinced that everyone is looking at you and judging you. I know that I become hyper-aware of my rapid heart rate, sweaty palms, and general physical discomfort. Unfortunately, these sensations make you even more aware of how nervous you're feeling, triggering even more anxiety!

One way to step outside of yourself is to redirect your attention away from you and onto other people. By transferring your focus away from your fears and past social experiences and on to the people you're speaking to, you can get out of your head. The more you concentrate on what's happening around you, the less you'll be affected by your thoughts and feelings. Do your best to engage in the conversation and make a genuine connection. Listen to what is being said and not to your negative thoughts.

Remember that anxiety isn't as visible as you think. Even if someone notices that you're nervous, that doesn't mean they'll judge you or think badly of you. Chances are you're not the only person who is feeling nervous. Try to stay present and fight the urge to judge or criticize yourself. Instead of beating yourself up about something you said or wish you'd said, give yourself a break. When you find yourself wishing you could have a do-over or are being too hard on yourself, imagine a friend coming to you and expressing the same thoughts that you're having. What words of encouragement would you tell them? Chances are your instincts to help your friend would lead you to say something like "Everybody says awkward things sometimes."

Social Anxiety Fact Checking

Since worries are thoughts that lead to anxious feelings, one way to manage your social anxiety is to challenge your worry-related thoughts. Use the following questions to try out this anxiety management strategy.

What are you worried about?

_____

_____

What evidence do you have that it will come true?

_____

_____

What's the absolute <u>worst</u> that could happen if it did come true?

_____

_____

_____

What's most likely to happen if your worry does come true?

_____

_____

_____

What's the likelihood that you'll be okay (in a day, a week, a month, or a year)?

_____

_____

_____

_____

_____

Anxiety in teens is very common.

About 33% of teenagers suffer from anxiety.

Tracking My Social Anxiety Triggers

Over the next week, pay close attention to your feelings and what causes you to feel socially anxious. At the end of each day, write down one anxiety trigger, and rate the intensity level of your anxiety on a scale of 1 – 10 by circling the relevant number. A #1 is not at all anxious, and a #10 is the highest possible level of anxiety.

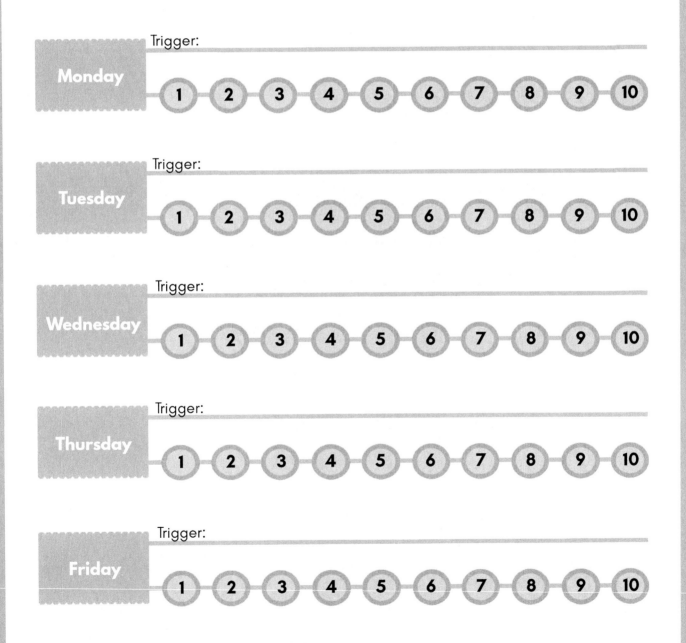

Monday

Trigger:

1   2   3   4   5   6   7   8   9   10

Tuesday

Trigger:

1   2   3   4   5   6   7   8   9   10

Wednesday

Trigger:

1   2   3   4   5   6   7   8   9   10

Thursday

Trigger:

1   2   3   4   5   6   7   8   9   10

Friday

Trigger:

1   2   3   4   5   6   7   8   9   10

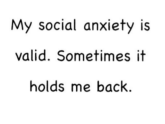

My Social Anxiety Thermometer

Let's use the thermometer again, except this time, we'll use it to measure the intensity of your social anxiety levels. As you think about your anxiety, think of words to describe how your anxiety feels at 25%, 50%, 75%, and 100%. For example, 25% is a little unpleasant, 50% is hard but tolerable, 75% is very uncomfortable, and 100% is intolerable. For each of these intensities, pay particular attention to how you physically experience the anxiety in your body. Does your mouth get dry? Does your mind go blank? Do you struggle to find something to say?

Once you have filled in your thermometer on the next page, you can use it any time to identify your social anxiety levels.

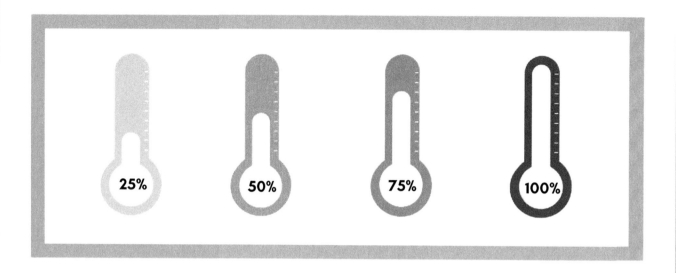

My Social Anxiety Levels

At 25% I feel: _____

My body cues are: _____

At 50% I feel: _____

My body cues are: _____

At 75% I feel: _____

My body cues are: _____

At 100% I feel: _____

My body cues are: _____

WHEN YOU LET ANGER GET THE BEST OF YOU, IT BRINGS OUT THE WORST IN YOU.

Chapter 5

UNDERSTANDING YOUR ANGER AND FRUSTRATION

Everyone gets angry. It's a normal emotion. At its core, anger is the expression of an underlying need or want that hasn't been met. Understanding our anger can be difficult since the cause of our anger is not often immediately obvious. For example, anger is often associated with frustration. We can also get angry when things don't happen the way we want them to or when people don't act the way we would expected them to.

The Art of Anger Management

There is a common misconception that anger is a volatile emotion that we have no control over. But you have more control over your anger than you think. By gaining insights into the source and real reasons for your anger and using the anger management tools set out in this chapter, you can learn to express your emotions without hurting others. You can also learn to control your temper so that it doesn't negatively affect your life.

Many people think that anger management is about learning to suppress your anger. But never getting angry is not a healthy goal. You will feel anger, regardless of how hard you try to avoid it. The goal of anger management isn't to suppress feelings of anger but rather to understand how to express anger in a healthy way.

Learning to understand, control and express your anger appropriately will help you build better relationships, achieve your goals, and lead a healthier, more fulfilling life.

MYTH: I can't help myself. Anger isn't something you can control.

FACT: You can't always control the situation you're in or how it makes you feel, but you can control how you express your anger. Even if someone is pushing your buttons, you always have a choice in how you respond.

Reining In Your Anger

Anger is a normal, healthy emotion. Like any emotion, it conveys a message. Anger tells you that a situation is upsetting, or unfair. Although it's normal to feel angry when you've been mistreated or wronged, anger becomes a problem when you express it in a way that harms yourself or others. It can also impair your judgment and get in the way of your success. Uncontrolled anger can also harm the way people see you.

Chronic anger that flares up all the time or spirals out of control can have a negative effect on your:

- **Physical health.** Always being angry makes you more susceptible to heart disease, diabetes, a weakened immune system, insomnia, and high blood pressure. According to a recent study, people who have less control over their anger tend to have their wounds heal more slowly.

- **Mental health.** Chronic anger takes enormous amounts of mental energy and clouds your thinking, making it harder to enjoy life. It can also lead to stress, depression, and other mental health problems.

- **Relationships.** Anger can damage and jeopardize friendships and relationships. Some people express anger verbally by shouting, name-calling, or saying ugly things, which can be very hurtful and damaging to relationships. Other people may show anger in passive ways, such as ignoring people, giving people the silent treatment, or sulking, which are not behaviours that people like.

Becoming Aware of Your Anger Warning Signs

While you may feel that you explode into anger without warning, there are physical warning signs in your body that give you signals. Becoming aware of when your temper is starting to boil over will allow you to take steps to manage your anger before it gets out of control. Pay attention to the way your body feels anger. Common physical symptoms of anger include:

- Feeling clammy.

- Knots in your stomach.

- Breathing faster.

- Shaking or trembling.

- A pounding head.

- Muscle tension.

- Feeling hot or flushed.

- Increased heart rate.

- Clenching your hands.

- Grinding your teeth.

Stressful events don't excuse anger, but understanding how these events affect you can help you take control of your environment. Look at your routine and try to identify activities, times of day, people, places, or situations that trigger angry feelings. When you identify your anger triggers, you can find ways to avoid them.

Exploring Your Anger

Learning to identify the thought patterns that fuel your anger will allow you to reframe how you think and respond to triggering situations. This activity will help you to improve your ability to identify and understand your anger so that you can begin to find ways to manage it. In the spaces below, list four things, circumstances, or thoughts that make you angry.

1 _____

2 _____

3 _____

4 _____

Now go back and rate them all, using #1 for the most challenging situation and #4 for the easiest to manage. Pick a situation that you labeled as #1 or #2 (one of the hardest, that causes the most anger), and answer the following questions with that situation in mind.

What are some of the thoughts you have in this situation? For example, do you feel you were misunderstood? Were you treated fairly?

_____

_____

_____

_____

What are some of the feelings that you have in this situation? Include both physical sensations, such as trembling and emotional feelings, such as frustration.

_____

_____

_____

_____

Now, consider all of the situations you previously listed that make you feel angry, as well as any other scenarios you can think of and respond to the following questions.

How do you usually respond when you're angry? What actions do you typically take?

_____

_____

_____

_____

How do your family members behave when they're angry? What about your friends? Take a moment and think about how other people in your life act when they're angry.

_____

_____

_____

Getting Acquainted With Your Anger

Describe a recent situation when you experienced difficulty controlling your anger.

_____

_____

_____

_____

Was there anything you could have changed about this situation to make it less upsetting?
Was there anything you could have changed to make it more pleasant? For example,
avoiding the situation or asking for help.

_____

_____

_____

_____

List the things you were unable to change about this situation? What didn't you have control
over?

_____

_____

_____

Tackling Your Anger

Identify five situations that make you angry. Build up the intensity by starting with an event that makes you feel irritable and ending with an event that makes you furious. Identify how your body feels in each of those situations. Notice how the intensity of your emotions change.

List any strategies you can use to calm yourself and to gain control of your thoughts and feelings.

Intensity	Trigger	Sensation	Calming Strategy
1	Irritable		
2	Annoyed		
3	Angry		
4	Enraged		
5	Furious		

Negative Thought Patterns That Can Trigger Anger

You may think that external factors, such as other people's insensitive actions, cause you to get angry. But anger problems have less to do with what happens to you than how you interpret, respond, and perceive what happened. Common negative thinking patterns that trigger and fuel anger include:

- **Overgeneralizing.** Making sweeping over-generalizations. For example, everyone is always mean to me. All my teachers dislike me.

- **Rigid Expectations.** Having rigid views about how a situation will go, such as expecting a situation to go exactly as planned. Since things rarely go to plan, when the reality doesn't line up with your expectation, it can lead to anger, disappointment and resentment.

- **Jumping To Conclusions.** Sometimes we're too quick to jump to conclusions and to make assumptions about other people's intentions and behavior towards us. For example, assuming that someone deliberately set out to upset you.

- **Collecting Straws.** Sometimes we can let small irritations and annoyances build and build and build until we reach the "final straw," and end up exploding, often over something relatively minor.

- **The Blame Game.** When anything bad happens, no matter how trivial, telling ourselves that life isn't fair or blaming others for our problems rather than taking responsibility for our own lives.

Give Yourself A Reality Check

Sometimes it's easy to lose perspective. Negative feelings can cloud our minds and consume our thoughts. As our stress mounts, our triumphs and accomplishments, the lessons we've learned, the hard times we've overcome, and how we've grown are overlooked and overshadowed by an unhealthy mentality. Below is an activity to help ground you and give you a reality check.

When you start getting upset about something, take a moment to think about the situation. Ask yourself:

- [ ] Is taking action worth my time and effort?

- [ ] Is it really worth getting angry about it?

- [ ] Is my response appropriate to the situation?

- [ ] Is there anything I can do about it?

- [ ] Is it worth ruining the rest of my day?

- [ ] How important is it in the grand scheme of things?

Practice Self-Kindness and Compassion

Sometimes we get angry at ourselves for feeling a certain way. We can feel ashamed, embarrassed, or sad that we've let our emotions get the better of us and have acted in a way that doesn't reflect who we are. Often, when we're angry, what we need is kindness and understanding. Don't forget that you can provide this to yourself by being compassionate to yourself. Practicing self-kindness helps you be a good friend to yourself and comfort yourself in the same way you would support a sad or upset friend.

Close your eyes and think of a recent situation that caused you to get angry. As you think of this moment, put a hand on your heart and say, "Ouch!" (either aloud or silently).

Next, think about all the people around the world who are feeling the same as you. People who may be feeling angry and frustrated at themselves. People who may be judging themselves harshly. Notice how this makes you feel empathetic towards them.

Now say something kind to yourself. Something reassuring like, "You're too hard on yourself, give yourself a break." Or "Although I'm feeling awful today, things will get better. I have lots of awesome things to look forward to."

Now, open your eyes, and focus on how you feel.

What did you notice?

Do you feel a little better?

KINDNESS CHANGES EVERYTHING

When you
THINK
POSITIVE
good things
HAPPEN

Chapter 6

CONNECTING YOUR THOUGHTS, FEELINGS, AND BEHAVIORS

Thoughts, Feelings, And Behaviors

All situations involve our thoughts, feelings, and behaviors. Our thoughts, feelings, and behaviors are linked and interconnected.

Thoughts: words, ideas or opinions that you tell yourself.

Feelings: the physical and emotional reactions in your body.

Behaviors: the actions that you take or the things that you do.

Since thoughts, feelings, and behaviors are all interconnected, they influence each other. Visualize each as the side of a triangle. You can start with any of the sides, and there's a connected reaction in the other two sides. When we think something, this thought affects how we feel, and how we feel influences how we behave.

This chain works the same if you start with a feeling; your mood results in both thoughts and actions. For example, if you are furious, you may be unable to control your negative thoughts and may say something in the heat of the moment that you later regret.

Keep in mind that sometimes failing to take action can also result in having thoughts and feelings. For example, feeling guilty about not having walked your dog.

Let's apply the thoughts, feelings, and behavior triangle to a concrete example. Emily got an F on her French test. Below is one way in which Emily could respond.

THOUGHTS

- I'm going to fail French
- I'm not intelligent
- My parents will be upset

BEHAVIORS

- Starts to hate French
- Avoids telling parents
- Doesn't ask for help

FEELINGS

- Anxious
- Embarassed
- Frustrated

How could Emily's thoughts and feelings have influenced her behavior in this situation?

_____

_____

_____

_____

Since thoughts, feelings, and behaviors are all connected, a change in any one of them can influence the others. By changing your thoughts you can change your feelings and behaviors.

A simple strategy to help you analyze your thoughts is to ask yourself:

 Is this thought **T**rue?

 Is this thought **H**elpful?

 Is this thought **I**nspiring?

 Is this thought **N**ecessary?

 Is this thought **K**ind?

What thoughts would Emily have had when she got an F on her French test?

• I'm going to fail French.

• I'm not intelligent.

• My parents will be upset with me.

Are these thoughts true? Are these the only possibilities?

_____

_____

_____

Are these thoughts **helpful**? Does thinking this way help Emily achieve her goal of doing well on her next French exam?

_____

_____

_____

Are Emily's thoughts **inspiring**? Do these thoughts motivate or encourage Emily to perform better on her next French exam?

_____

_____

_____

Are these thoughts **necessary**? Which of Emily's thoughts could undermine her in this situation?

_____

_____

_____

Are her thoughts **kind**? Is this how you would speak to a friend who is in this situation?

_____

_____

_____

What are some different ways that Emily could think about this situation that would be more true, helpful, inspiring, necessary and kind?

_____

_____

_____

Now let's look at how Emily's situation could be different if she replaced her unhelpful and negative thoughts with positive thoughts.

THOUGHTS

- I'll study more
- I wasn't the only person who failed
- This setback won't discourage me
- I can still do well in French class

BEHAVIORS

- Ask teacher for help
- Make flashcards
- Study more

FEELINGS

- Hopeful
- Anxious
- Optimistic

Notice that while Emily still feels anxious about failing her French class, reframing how she was thinking about her setback led to different behaviors (actions).

How could these specific actions help Emily achieve her goal of doing better on her next French test?

_____

_____

_____

Let's apply this approach to a situation in your life. Think of a recent situation that you found challenging or stressful. Fill in the spaces below to explore what your thoughts, feelings, and behaviors were in this situation.

Situation: _____

_____

My thoughts: _____

_____

_____

My feelings: _____

_____

_____

My Behaviors:

_____

_____

_____

Now, let's analyze how helpful your thoughts were in this situation.

Are these thoughts **true**? Are these thoughts the only possible result?

_____

_____

_____

_____

_____

Are these thoughts **helpful**? Did these thoughts help you get closer to achieving your goal?

_____

_____

_____

_____

_____

_____

Are these thoughts **inspiring**? Do these thoughts motivate and encourage you?

_____

_____

_____

Are these thoughts **necessary**? Which of your thoughts are the least helpful in dealing with this situation? Could any of these thoughts sabotage you?

_____

_____

_____

Are your thoughts **kind**? Is this the way that you would speak to a friend or relative who is in this situation? Are you being understanding and compassionate towards yourself?

_____

_____

_____

Which of your thoughts could you change to be more helpful, inspiring or positive in this situation?

_____

_____

_____

Which of your old thoughts could you change to be more helpful or positive in this situation?

Old Thought　　　　　　　　　**Helpful / Positive Thought**

How could reframing your thoughts in this situation lead to experiencing different feelings?

How could different thoughts and feelings change your behaviors (actions)? Could the outcome of this situation have been any different if your actions were different?

Thoughts vs. Feelings

Below is an activity to help ground you and give you a reality check. Although thoughts and feelings are closely related, they are not the same. Distinguishing between thoughts and feelings can be confusing, because people use the terms interchangeably.

People often express their thoughts by saying "I feel ...." For example, if someone says, "I feel that she deserves a reward for doing well on her history test." In this circumstance, the person is using "I feel" to mean a thought, and not a feeling. In other words, the person is expressing a judgment or opinion about a situation (doing well on the history test). When people use "I feel" in this context, what they actually mean to say is "I think that ...." or "I believe that...."

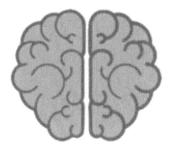

A **thought** is an idea, judgment, or opinion that we use to understand our feelings and experiences. Thoughts are basically the little voice in your head that comments on your life. For example, thinking about giving a speech in front of your class may cause you to worry.

On the other hand, a **feeling** is an emotional state or reaction. Feelings often cause a physical response. For example, when you are feeling nervous, you may feel jittery.

The following activity will help you to practice distinguishing between your thoughts and feelings.

	Thought	Feeling
I feel calm and relaxed.		
I feel that I'd like scuba diving.		
I feel like I could learn to play chess.		
I feel nervous.		
I feel like I'd make a good scientist.		
I feel happy.		
I feel that my teacher is very strict.		
I feel that I'm too hard on myself.		
I feel that I aced my Spanish exam.		
I feel shy.		

Anxiety Or Worry?

People often use the words anxiety and worry interchangeably, which can be confusing. Although both terms are related, there is an important distinction between them. **Anxiety** is your body's physical and emotional reaction to stress or danger. Anxiety is a feeling.

On the other hand, a **worry** is made up of the thoughts, judgments, or perspectives about the situation causing you anxiety. Worries are thoughts you have about unpleasant situations.

Below are some things to keep in mind about anxiety and worry.

Anxiety is experienced in your body.

A **worry** is experienced in your head.

Anxiety is persistent, even when the concerns are unrealistic and unlikely to happen.

Anxiety Or Worry: Which Is It?

Below is an activity that will help you to distinguish anxiety from worry and will help you to understand how they're related. Imagine that you're running for class president and are about to give a speech in front of your whole school.

Anxiety: How would you feel in this situation?

_____

_____

_____

Describe the physical sensation of this feeling in your body?

_____

_____

_____

Worry: What would you be thinking?

_____

_____

_____

_____

Worry Log

Some worries don't bother us very much, whereas some worries can consume our thoughts and keep us up at night. One of the best ways to take charge of your worries is to identify whether you are worrying about something serious or worrying about something that isn't that important. Once you identify the type of worry, you can decide if your concerns are worth worrying about, and if so, you can come up with a plan to address how to tackle them.

For the next six days, keep track of the worries you have. Write down at least two worries that you have each day, no matter how big or small. For each worry, rate how much anxiety it causes you using the scale on this page.

This exercise will also help you to identify the types of concerns, issues and problems that you worry about.

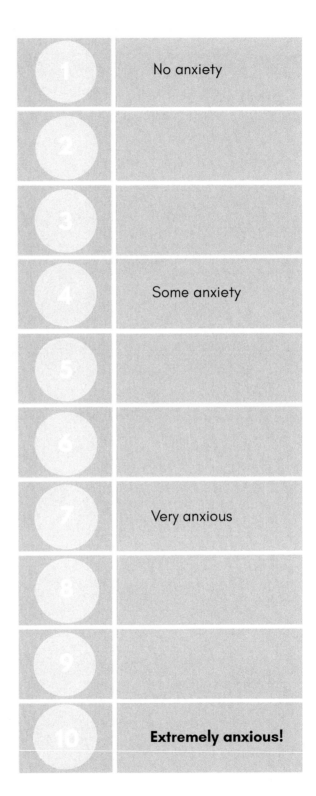

1	No anxiety
2	
3	
4	Some anxiety
5	
6	
7	Very anxious
8	
9	
10	**Extremely anxious!**

Day 1

Worry 1:

Anxiety Rating:

Worry 2:

Anxiety Rating:

Day 2

Worry 1:

Anxiety Rating:

Worry 2:

Anxiety Rating:

Day 3

Worry 1:

Anxiety Rating:

Worry 2:

Anxiety Rating:

Day 4	**Worry 1:**	**Anxiety Rating:**
	Worry 2:	**Anxiety Rating:**
Day 5	**Worry 1:**	**Anxiety Rating:**
	Worry 2:	**Anxiety Rating:**
Day 6	**Worry 1:**	**Anxiety Rating:**
	Worry 2:	**Anxiety Rating:**

Let It Go

Some worries are so minor that they aren't worth worrying about. Now that you have the skills to distinguish small worries from big worries, consider unburdening yourself and reducing your anxiety by letting go of some of your smaller worries.

Visualize inflating a balloon. As you blow up the balloon, imagine that you are transferring your worries into the balloon. Once you have filled the balloon with your worries, imagine yourself going outside and letting your worry-filled balloon drift up, up, up into the sky. Watch it gradually disappear.

Write the worries that you want to let go of on the balloons below.

Escape-Aid

Sometimes things can get too overwhelming. Instead of wasting your time and energy on worrying, find fun ways to distract yourself. An escape-aid could be spending time on social media, binge-watching a TV show, or reading a book. It can be any activity that you enjoy. If you are struggling to come up with some ideas try some of the activities listed on pages 54 and 55.

On the plasters below, list some of the things you can do to help you escape.

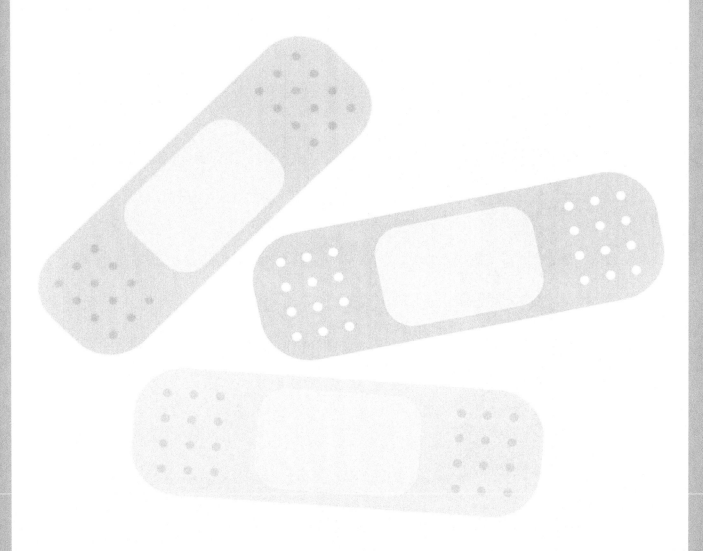

Lock Away Your Worries For Safe Keeping

Worrying about something you have no control over rarely leads to a solution. Take time to acknowledge your worries and to explore the roots of your worries or problems. Once you know the most important things you worry about, ask yourself if your worries are solvable. If there is nothing you can do to solve your worries, resolve to give yourself a mental break from worrying. To do this, imagine placing your worries in a locked safe for safekeeping. By temporarily giving yourself a break from the burden and weight of your worries, you are allowing yourself to have some much needed carefree time.

REPLACE YOUR NEGATIVE THOUGHTS, WITH POSITIVE THOUGHTS.

Chapter 7

REFRAMING YOUR NEGATIVE THOUGHTS

Our mental health and wellbeing depend on our ability to manage our thoughts, regulate our emotions, and control our behavior. Of course, this is much easier said than done. At some point in our lives, every one of us will struggle with our mental health. However, by learning to recognize and manage your thinking errors, you'll build the mental strength to overcome the setbacks and challenges that life will inevitably throw at you.

Challenging Your Thinking Errors and Mix-Ups

Thinking errors are unhealthy thinking patterns that are twisted, distorted, or false. Since our thoughts greatly influence how we feel and how we behave, listening to and believing distorted thoughts can significantly impact our emotions, behaviors, and views.

One of the greatest gifts you can give yourself is to recognize and eliminate your harmful thinking errors so that you can live your best life. Below are 12 of the most common thinking errors:

- **Fortune Telling.** This is when we predict that things will turn out badly, even if we have absolutely no proof that this will be the case. This thinking error can set us up to fail. If we believe things will go wrong, we may inadvertently act in a way that causes things to go wrong. For example, you want to invite Kalinda to go to a concert with you, but you convince yourself that she's going to say no. So, you don't ask her and end up missing out on an opportunity to hang out with someone you want to get to know better.

- **Disqualifying The Positive.** This is when nine good things happen and one bad thing happens, yet we only focus on the one bad thing. In other words, positive experiences don't count as much as perceived negative experiences. Filtering out and dismissing the positive can prevent us from establishing a realistic perception of a situation. Developing a balanced outlook requires us to notice both the positive and the negative.

- **Catastrophizing.** This is when we see things as being much worse than they are. In other words, we blow things out of proportion. For example, you text a friend (who usually responds quickly). When you don't hear back from her for a few hours, you convince yourself that she is mad at you and will never speak to you again.

- **All-Or-Nothing Thinking.** This is when we only see things as being black or white. We may take the view that we have to be perfect, or we're a complete failure! There is no middle ground. Instead of seeing things only in extremes, we need to recognize the shades of gray.

- **Overgeneralizing.** This is when someone reaches a general conclusion based on a single incident or a single piece of evidence. If something terrible happens just once, we then expect it to happen over and over again. We may see a single, unpleasant event as part of a never-ending pattern of defeat. For example, if you bomb an exam, you conclude that you're a terrible student who won't get into any university.

- **Magnifying The Negative.** This is when we magnify and zoom in on the negative aspects of our day. We may declare that we had a bad day, despite having had a few positive experiences throughout the day. Or we may look back at our performance and say it was terrible because we made a single mistake. Magnifying the negative can prevent you from establishing a realistic outlook on a situation.

- **Jumping To Conclusions.** This is when we assume that we know what another person is feeling and thinking and exactly why they act the way they do. We may even believe that we can determine how others feel towards us, as though we can read their mind. For example, you may conclude that a classmate is holding a grudge against you, but don't try to determine if this assumption is correct.

- **Emotional Reasoning.** This is when we believe that our emotions accurately reflect the reality of the situation. For example, "I feel guilty, so I must have done something bad," or "I feel afraid, so I must be in a dangerous situation.

- **Labeling.** This is when we take an overgeneralization and put a label on it. For example, since you didn't know the answer to a question in class, you decide that you're stupid and a terrible student.

- **Should Statements.** This is when we have a set of expectations about ourselves or someone else that "should" be met, but then feel angry or guilty when these expectations aren't met. For example, you decide that you should have lots more followers on Instagram, and then feel bad that you don't have as many followers as you'd like.

- **Personalization.** This is when we feel that we're to blame for anything and everything that goes wrong. This includes blaming ourselves for things that are beyond our control. For example, you find out that the friend you trusted with a secret has broken your confidence. Instead of being upset with your friend for telling people your secret, you blame yourself for trusting her.

- **Unreal Ideal.** This is when we unfairly and unrealistically compare ourselves to other people. For example Kylie Jenner started her makeup company and bought her first home when she was 17; since I haven't done these things, I must be a loser.

Which of the 12 thinking errors have you used over the last week?

_____

_____

_____

_____

_____

_____

Which thinking error is the one that you use the most?

_____

_____

Which thinking error would you like to change first? Why?

_____

_____

_____

Reframing Your Thoughts

Pay close attention to your thoughts for one whole day. Then fill in the thought bubbles below. What thoughts did you have? Were you kind to yourself? If you had negative thoughts about yourself, try to rewrite these thoughts to be more positive. If you struggle to come up with positive thoughts, ask yourself what you would say to a good friend. After you complete this activity, resolve to be more aware of your thoughts over the next week. Are you having more positive thoughts? Are you being a better friend to yourself? If any negative thoughts sneak in, try to capture and reframe them into positives.

Flipping Negative Thoughts Into Positive Thoughts

The secret to flipping unhappy thoughts into hopeful ones is to decipher your negative thoughts and then turning these negative thoughts into positive advice. In other words, the type of advice you would give to a friend.

For example:

What I Think	What I Really Think	Flip It!
This is too hard. I give up!	I'm frustrated that I'm finding this hard.	If I keep trying, I'll eventually nail it.
I wish I was like everyone else.	Standing out makes me uncomfortable.	I like being unique. I'm my own person.
I'll never learn to ride a bike.	Other people don't struggle like I do.	I'm not giving up. I know I can do this!

Now it's your turn. Each time a negative thought tries to stop you from doing something, write it down in the table on the next page. Can you work out why you're having this thought? How can you turn it into a positive thought?

If you get stuck, imagine that your best friend has come to you with the problem. What advice would you give?

What I Really Think	What I Think	Flip It!

Controlling Your Thoughts

Do you ever wish that you could dial down the intensity of your thoughts or slow down your racing thoughts? This activity will help you to identify your worries and identify coping skills to improve how you react to these thoughts. In the high volume section, write down a loud thought that's bothering you. Then identify which coping skills you could use to turn down the volume to a medium level. List these skills in the medium volume section. Finally, in the low volume box, write down what could help to turn the volume down to low.

High	Medium	Low

Stop - Identify - Reframe

Identify a thinking error that you've recently had, and write it in the first box. Now identify which part of the unhealthy thinking error is false or distorted. Write down these errors in the second box. Now think of how to reframe your negative thought into a positive one. Place your positive thought into the last box.

STOP

Write down a recent thinking error.

IDENTIFY

Identify the false or distorted part of your thinking error.

REFRAME

Reframe the negative thought into a positive one.

Reframing Sad Thoughts

In the box below, write down a recent problem that made you sad. Write about any negative thoughts you had, how you reacted, and how your body felt. In the second box, reframe any negative thoughts into positive ones, list any constructive actions you could have taken (such as asking for help), and how your body would have felt if you had used your coping skills.

My negative thought:

How I reacted:

How my body felt:

Reframing my negative thought into a positive one:

Constructive actions I can take to cope:

How my body would feel after using my coping skills:

Test Your Thinking

Sometimes you may find it incredibly hard to stop negative thoughts. When you get bombarded with negative thoughts, it can be hard to turn them off or switch to a different thought. One tool that you may find helpful is to challenge the thinking error by testing your thinking. Fill in the below chart to identify your most common negative thoughts.

List your most frequent negative thought.

On a scale from 1 to 10, how strongly do you believe this thought?

Is your thought a thinking error? If so, which one?

Is any part of your negative thought false or distorted?

What would you advise a friend who had the same negative thought?

On a scale from 1 to 10, how accurate do you think this thought is now?

Helpful Thinking

Replace a negative thought with a positive thought for each scenario set out below.

You have to give a presentation in front of your whole class.

Negative thought:

Positive thought:

You have an unexpected change to your routine.

Negative thought:

Positive thought:

You accidentally drop your phone and crack the phone screen.

Negative thought:

Positive thought:

You forget to turn in the homework that you spent hours completing.

Negative thought:

Positive thought:

Become An Optimist

This glass is half full (rather than half empty). There are times when it's difficult to see the positives in a situation. In this activity, you'll acknowledge your negative thoughts and then reframe your negative thoughts with positive thoughts so that you see the glass as half full. In the space below, list a negative thought, and reframe it into a positive one.

Negative Thought	Positive Thought
Nobody likes me.	Maya saved a seat for me at the lunch table today and Omar offered to lend me his class notes when I missed a day of school last week.

Good News: Looking On The Bright Side

A simple and easy way to brighten your day is to focus on positive news. Spend 15 minutes searching for uplifting and inspiring news stories on the Internet. Write the headline on a sticky note. Find a wall in your room that you can designate as a positive zone and stick your good news notes on it.

Teen girl posts uplifting notes on suicide bridge and helps save six lives!

Autistic teen wins Wainright Prize for nature writing.

Greta Thunberg sails across the Atlantic Ocean to attend climate change conference.

The population of the endangered black rhino is slowly increasing.

Teenage girl wins top prize and a scholarship in Science Fair.

Teen girl fights period poverty by launching campaign for free sanitary products in schools.

Autistic blogger starts online petition to fight against sexualized images of girls and women in the media.

Transgender teen climate activist gives inspiring speech at the United Nations Climate Change Convention.

A TRUE FRIEND ACCEPTS WHO YOU ARE AND HELPS YOU BECOME WHO YOU SHOULD BE.

Chapter 8

HOW TO MAKE FRIENDS

· ·

Autism and Friendships

There's a common misconception that autistic individuals are anti-social and don't want to have friends. This is untrue. Most of us want to have friendships, and a sense of belonging, just like other teenagers. Friendships can be extremely positive and beneficial. A friend is someone you can talk to about your interests, someone who gives you advice and guidance and supports you during difficult times. Friendships can make navigating our teenage years easier.

What distinguishes us from other teenagers is that social skills and interactions don't come naturally to us. Many autistic people find it tough to make and keep friends. Most of us find social rules confusing, struggle to understand body language and don't pick up on subtle social cues. As you now know, we often also experience social anxiety. So, it's hardly surprising that we find developing and maintaining relationships challenging.

Furthermore, our social skill difficulties become even more challenging in our teenage years when social interactions become more complex and harder to decipher. Since, most of us want to be like other teenagers our social difficulties can be especially frustrating. We want to have friends who understand, encourage, and support us. We want to have fun. We want to have the typical high school experience. Instead, may of us miss out on the traditional high school experience. Many autistic young people feel lonely and socially isolated from their classmates. In high school, I found it much harder to read social situations, especially in group settings. My fear of misinterpreting social situations and doing or saying something awkward or embarrassing left me riddled with social anxiety. This fear was made worse by being frequently bullied at school. I was always worried that bringing unwanted attention to myself would lead to more bullying.

Being bullied at school is a real concern for many autistic young people. In high school, there's a huge emphasis on fitting in and being like everyone else. Students who are different or who stand out of the crowd are often targeted. According to the 2017 Bullying Survey by Ditch the Label of over 10,000 young people, 75% of autistic young people reported being bullied at school. So, if you've ever been bullied for being autistic, know that it's not your fault and that you're not alone. Chapter 10 has advice and information how to deal with bullying, which I hope you find helpful.

In this chapter, I'll be sharing tips and tricks that you can use to make and develop friendships. However, I want to emphasize that not every autistic person wants to have friends. You may find that there are times when you want friends and times when you prefer your own compnay. Some autistic people aren't interested in having friends because they find making and maintaining friendships too stressful, demanding and exhausting. This is a valid choice. I went through stages where I found making and keeping friends too emotionally draining and decided to avoid socializing to safeguard my mental health. Since people who aren't autistic believe that you must have friends to be happy, I was frequently pressured to socialize.

Autistic people have different needs, which are just as valid as those of non-autistic people. If you feel that you need to take a social break, explain to the people around you that this is a decision you've made so that you can take care of yourself and you can recharge your social battery.

What Makes A True Friend?

Friendships can be very confusing. Sometimes someone will say that they're your friend, but not act like a true friend. This happened to me more times than I care to remember. Just because someone spends time with you and says that they're your friend doesn't mean it's true. Sometimes they can be false friends (frenemies) or bullies in disguise. Since we are vulnerable to being taken advantage of by people who don't have good intentions, it's important to know what qualities to look for in a friendship. In order to help you identify what makes a true friend, below is a list of qualities to look for:

- Friends are people who are interested in us and our lives.

- You usually have at least one shared interest, and they enjoy talking about that interest with you.

- Friends listen to you and make you feel good about yourself.

- You enjoy spending time with them.

- Friends usually have personality traits that you like, such as being kind and thoughtful.

- Friends include you and don't just reach out to you when they need something.

- Friends stand up for you and have your back.

- They encourage, support, and accept you, even when you're at your worst.

- They don't judge you, put you down, or belittle you.

- Friendships are always equal and balanced; a person who always takes help and support from you but doesn't do the same in return is not a true friend.

- Friends are genuinely happy for you when something good happens to you. They celebrate your achievements and successes.

- A good friend can help you understand your triggers and anxieties and support you in coping with them.

- A good friend can also help you to improve your social skills and guide you through socially complex situations.

- Friends are loyal, dependable, and trustworthy.

- Friends are understanding, forgiving, and accept you just as you are.

Suppose you realize that a friendship is one-sided or that the person who claims to be your friend doesn't display many of the qualities listed above. If you find yourself in this situation, you may want to reevaluate that relationship. This is especially true if the person makes you feel bad about yourself.

You deserve to have genuine friends that accept you, make you feel good about yourself, and wish the best for you.

SURROUND YOURSELF WITH PEOPLE WHO CARE ABOUT YOU - NOT JUST THOSE WHO SAY THEY DO, BUT THOSE WHO SHOW IT.

Top 10 Tips For Being A Good Friend

Like any relationship, friendships are a two-way street. Below are 10 tips on being a good friend:

- **Be a Good Listener**. Take the time to truly understand and support your friend when she or he is talking to you. It's important to make sure that you're listening as much as you're talking about yourself. If you're monopolizing every conversation, your friend isn't getting anything out of the relationship. It's vital that you truly listen and are not just waiting for your friend to finish talking so that you can say what you want to say. If you're simply waiting to speak, your friend will pick up on this. I suggest that you try to strike a balance by letting your friend talk about half of the time. Unfortunately, if your friend feels like they can't get a word in when they're talking to you, it'll be hard to have a balanced friendship. If you find that you frequently accidentally interrupt your friends, say something like, "Oh-I'm so sorry, go on."

- **Be Dependable**. One of the most important aspects of being a good friend is being dependable. Your friend should be able to rely on you for encouragement and support. Nobody wants to be friends with someone who isn't there for them. Your friends should always feel like they can count on you, especially when the going gets tough. If you're only there for the fun and care-free times, you'll be no more than a superficial, fair-weather friend.

- **Be Loyal.** Always be loyal to your friends, and be prepared to defend them if others start gossiping about them. If your friend tells you something in confidence, don't talk about it with anyone else. After all, you wouldn't be happy if someone you confided in told everyone your secret. If you get a reputation for being a gossip, your friends will stop confiding in you and may even decide that you can't be trusted.Once you loose someone's trust it's hard to earn it back.

It's also important not to criticize or speak badly about your friends behind their back. A good rule to live by is to never say anything about your friends that you wouldn't want to repeat to their face. Don't let others say bad things about your friends either. Until you've had a chance to hear their side of the story, treat any negative comments and gossip you hear about your friends with skepticism. If someone says something that shocks you, and that doesn't sound like something your friend would do or say, then respond with something like, "I know them, and that doesn't sound right. Let me talk to them. Until then, I would really appreciate it if you didn't spread this around."

- **Give Thoughtful Advice.** Being a good friend involves seeing your friend's situation from his or her perspective, and providing your advice without insisting that your friend do whatever you say. Although it's hard to do, try to avoid giving unsolicited advice to your friends. Instead, only share your advice when your friends have asked you for it. Giving unsolicited advice to your friends could be interpreted as you lecturing them and being too bossy and overbearing.

- **Disagree With Your Friend in a Respectful Way.** At some point, good friends will disagree with each other. After all, we all have different views and perspectives. A disagreement doesn't have to be a big deal. On the occasions when you don't see eye to eye, disagree respectfully, and be willing and open to seeing things from their perspective. Respect your friend's feelings and generally respect him or her as a person. Good friends show respect for each other by being openly and mutually supportive. Remember that you want to be a positive addition to your friends' lives. When a friend shares something that you find objectionable, or you disagree with their opinion, it's okay to say so. In a non-judgmental way, let your friend know what you think and why.

- **Be Generous**. Although you shouldn't be generous all the time, being generous with your time and affections is an essential aspect of being a good friend. Accommodate your friend's wishes whenever you can, provided this is done in a fair and balanced way. Do something nice for your friend to show how much you value their friendship, not because you want something in return. Reciprocate his or her acts of kindness with caring deeds of your own. If you get a reputation for being selfish, demanding, and only being around your friends when you need their help, people will be less likely to want to be your friend. A word of warning, there's a big difference between being generous at the right time and letting people take advantage of you. If you feel like you're always helping your friends and get nothing in return, then you may want to reevaluate that friendship.

- **Help Your Friends With Their Struggles.** Try to be the kind of person your friends turn to when they need support. Let your friends know that they can lean on you and that you can give them a shoulder to cry on when times are tough. If your friend feels less alone, it'll be easier for him or her to deal with their troubles. Don't feel pressured to fix your friend's problems. Sometimes just listening and being there for your friend is the best way to be a good friend.

- **Be There in a Time of Crisis.** If your friend is going through a crisis, try to help in any way that you can. For example, if your friend is sick and absent from school, take class notes for your friend. Part of supporting your friend through a crisis is providing emotional support. Sometimes it can be hard to know what to say. I suggest that you avoid saying something like, "Everything will be all right" unless you know this for sure. Giving false reassurance, no matter how well-intended, can make the situation worse. Instead, let your friend know you're there for them. You don't have to say anything if you can't find the right words. Sometimes just listening is enough.

A word of caution, make sure that your friend isn't someone who is always in the middle of a crisis. I had a friend who was always center stage because her life was a never-ending series of drama and problems, some of which I later found out she had made up. If you find that you are friends with someone who is always creating a problem so that they can be the focus of attention, you may want to reconsider this friendship.

- **Learn How to Take a Joke.** Jokes among friends can make a friendship fun and amusing. If you're sensitive to jokes or being teased, work on learning to accept well-intended and affectionate jokes and teasing. However, keep in mind that there is a fine line between teasing and bullying. Sometimes it can be hard to distinguish between the two. If your feelings are hurt, or you feel that the teasing is getting out of hand, don't be afraid to tell your friend. A good friend will be respectful of your feelings.

- **Be yourself!** Be the best version of yourself. Don't change who you are so you can make a new friend. Pretending to be someone that you're not will take a toll on you and will eventually backfire. Not being yourself also calls into question the entire friendship. After all, the friendship can't be authentic if you don't reveal the real you. Never forget that you're awesome the way you are. Don't settle or change yourself and your values to make friends. Be yourself. You are awesome and deserve to have friends that like you for who you are. There is only one you and that is your unique superpower!

DON'T CHANGE YOURSELF SO THAT OTHER PEOPLE WILL LIKE YOU. BE YOURSELF SO THAT THE RIGHT PEOPLE LOVE YOU.

What Do I Tell Myself?

Sometimes we can sabotage our ability to make friends by what we tell ourselves. If you tell yourself that you're too socially awkward, too anxious, too nerdy, etc..., you'll eventually convince yourself that no one will want to be your friend. Let's find out if there are unhelpful things that you tell yourself. Fill in any of the following blanks that you can relate to.

People won't want to be my friend because I'm _____

I don't have friend's because I'm _____

People don't like me because _____

Did you fill in one or more of the questions? If so, I'm sending you a big hug. Now fill in the following blanks:

I would make a good friend because I'm _____

People like me because _____

People would want to be friends with me because _____

Do you feel better? You should! You have many positive and wonderful traits. You can't be a good friend to someone else if you're not a good friend to yourself. So, remember to be kind to yourself!

BE KIND TO YOURSELF

Use Your Body Language

Some experts believe that up to 90% of face-to-face communication is non-verbal. In other words, much of what we communicate is conveyed through our facial expressions, eye contact, body language, and tone of voice. This can be particularly problematic for autistic people because many of us struggle with eye contact and with understanding body language. In addition, we often have a **flat affect** (this is when your facial expressions and tone of voice don't reflect what you're feeling).

When you're talking to someone, you have to show that you're interested in what they say. If you appear distracted and uninterested, your friend may think that you are being rude or that you're bored. This could upset your friend, especially if your friend is telling you something personal or that is particularly important to them. Below are a few tips on using body language that show that you're paying attention to what someone is telling you.

- Make eye contact (I find this tricky, so instead, I look at the person's forehead).

- Every so often, nod in agreement when they're speaking.

- Change your facial expressions depending on what they're telling you.

- Ask questions about what they're telling you.

- Try to subtly mirror / copy their body language.

Practicing varying my facial expressions helps to make it feel more natural.

If you have trouble changing your facial expressions, practice in the mirror. I watched TV shows to study how characters expressed their emotions and then practiced imitating these expressions until they felt less awkward and contrived.

How To Start A Conversation

Initiating and maintaining a conversation can be anxiety-inducing and overwhelming for anyone. However, this is especially true if you're autistic. A **conversation opener** is an introduction that you can use to begin a conversation. Since friendships are usually built around one or more shared interests, a good starting point is to talk about something you both share. For example, a class or a school activity or club.

Social conversations can be stressful because each one is different. Each conversation has so many variables that you can't control or know in advance. However, there are some common topics that most people generally feel comfortable talking about.

Here are some conversation starters that I frequently use.

- "Have you watched any cool movies or TV shows you'd recommend?"

- "What do you like to do in your spare time?"

- "Have you read anything interesting lately?"

- "Do you have any plans for this weekend?

- "What did you do this weekend?"

- "What music are you listening to?"

- "What's up?"

- "Do you have any pets?"

- "Who is your favorite influencer?"

- "Have you done anything exciting lately?

- "Are you interested in ...?"

- "What do you think about ...?"

- "What's your favorite ...?"

Conversation starters are a great way to initiate a conversation.

They make starting a conversation a lot less stressful.

How To Keep The Conversation Going

Once you start a conversation, keeping it going can be just as tricky. Below are some tips and tricks to keep a conversation going.

- **Ask Questions.** One easy tip that I frequently use to keep a conversation moving is to ask a question. When someone brings up a topic, ask questions about it. The beauty of this technique is that asking questions shows that are you listening to the speaker and also makes you appear interested and engaged. Another benefit of this technique is that if the person is talking about something you're unfamiliar with, you may learn something new.

- **Use Conversation Threading**. Conversation threading is when a person takes something someone says and turns it into a new comment or question. For example, if your friend says, "I went to the mall this weekend and bought some clothes and makeup in the sales." You could ask which mall she went to and which clothes and makeup she bought. You could also ask about the sales, such as whether certain items were on sale or whether she would recommend you buy something in the sales too. There are many different directions that the conversation can go with this sentence. So listen to threading statements that will allow you to weave out a conversation.

- **Have a List of Topics You Have In Common.** Another useful trick is to have a list of topics in mind that you can discuss. For example, you could discuss a TV show, the latest news about a celebrity, or any other interest you have in common.

How To End A Conversation

Sometimes it can be awkward to wrap up a conversation. Some autistic people struggle to know when a conversation has come to an end. Unfortunately, the end of a conversation is not always predictable. Knowing when to stop relies on many social rules, which may not be obvious and straightforward. Although people often use body language to show that they're ready to end the conversation or need to leave, we may miss these cues. So be mindful of the obvious signs, such as if the person starts looking at their watch or starts to walk away from you.

I find that it's helpful to have some conversation enders in my toolbox that I can use to end a conversation. Conversation enders are essential because they allow you to wrap up a conversation on a positive note.

Below are some great conversation enders.

- "Well, it was great talking to you."

- "See you later."

- "I really enjoyed catching up with you."

- "It was great chatting with you."

- "I have to go. Let's talk again sometime."

Top 10 Tips For A Fun Conversation

Here are some tips that I use to help make every conversation a positive one.

1   Show your interest by asking the person questions about themselves.

2   Use facial expressions and body language that match the conversation.

3   Laugh and respond to the other person's jokes.

4   Share stories that make your conversations come alive.

5   Roll with the punches, and try not to be too serious.

6   Make sure that your body language shows that you are paying attention.

7   Don't make the conversation all about you and your interests.

8   Relate to the person by telling them that you understand how they feel.

9   Try not to be too argumentative. Agree to disagree.

10   End on a positive note with a conversation ender.

BE GENTLE WITH YOURSELF, YOU'RE DOING THE BEST YOU CAN.

TRUE FRIENDSHIP ISN'T ABOUT BEING THERE WHEN IT'S CONVENIENT. IT'S ABOUT BEING THERE WHEN IT ISN'T.

Chapter 9

HOW TO MAINTAIN FRIENDSHIPS

●●●●●●●●●●●●●●●●●●●●●●●●●●●●●●●●

Top 10 Tips For Maintaining Your Friendships

Developing and maintaining friendships takes time and effort. If you regularly communicate and do your best to be a supportive and understanding friend, you can overcome any conflict and maintain your friendship for years to come.

Below are 10 tips that you can use to maintain your friendships.

- **Accept your friends for who they are.** Don't try to change your friend or make your friend see the world from your perspective. Recognize and celebrate what makes your friend special and unique. Try to appreciate the fresh perspective your friend can bring to your experiences, instead of expecting your friend to see everything from your point of view.

- **Recognize that good friendships go both ways.** It's not a good friendship if one of you is doing all the talking, and the other is doing all the listening all the time. Good friends make each other feel good and are equally balanced. A good friendship makes both of you feel valued and supported.

- **Go beyond the call of duty.** Recognize the moments when you need to go above and beyond to help your friend. Being there when your friend needs you will make your friendship grow and increases the likelihood that your friend will do the same for you in return. Remember that people will want to be a good friend to you if you're a good friend to them.

- **Make an effort.** Make sure that you pull your weight in your friendships. Don't wait for others to always invite you or for them to arrange something. Ask your new friends if they'd like to hang out. Invite them to take part in activities with you. Try to be proactive in staying in touch. Don't be afraid to take some initiative in reaching out. More often than not, your friends will be happy you did.

- **Don't take your friend for granted.** Don't just assume that your friend will be there for you when you need them if you don't regularly go out of your way to nurture the relationship. Cherish your friendships and be there for your friends during the ups and the downs. When you regularly see your friends, you can easily fall into a routine and take them for granted.

- **Tell them that you appreciate them.** If you don't voice your appreciation, some friends may feel like they're taken for granted. Remember to occasionally tell your friend how much you value and appreciate their friendship. You can do this by saying something like, "I really couldn't have done it without you. I really appreciate you being there for me."

- **Apologize when you've made a mistake.** Everyone makes mistakes. If you've said something unkind, or have disappointed a friend, the best thing to do is to own up to it. Although your friend may be hurt and upset with you, admitting to your mistake and sincerely apologizing can go a long way to putting your friendship back on track. When you apologize, take the time to explain that you didn't mean to hurt your friend's feelings, that you feel bad about having done so, and emphasize that you want to fix your relationship.

- **Use "I" statements in situations of conflict.** Friends will inevitably argue and disagree. In situations where you are trying to resolve a dispute, instead of focusing on what your friend did wrong, try shifting the focus onto yourself by describing how you're feeling about the situation. On page 156, I talk about the power of "I" statements.

- **Learn to forgive.** If you want your friendship to last, be willing to forgive your friend and move forward from most misunderstandings and disagreements. If you hold a grudge and let your bitterness and resentment build-up, it will gradually destroy your friendship. Recognize that nobody's perfect. As long as your friend is sincerely sorry, and didn't do something too horrible, do your best to move past it. If your friend did something unforgivable, it's better to end the relationship than to try to save a toxic friendship.

- **Give your friends some space when they need it.** Part of being a supportive friend involves understanding that your friend may not always want to spend time with you. Allowing each other the time to hang with other friends gives each of you breathing room. Be supportive if your friend wants to be alone or wants to hang out with other people. Try not to be clingy or needy. If you're clingy, controlling and possessive, it could damage your friendships. Although it's harder said than done, try not to get jealous or feel threatened if your friend has many other friends. Every relationship is unique, and that doesn't mean that your friend doesn't value and appreciate you.

Although it's important to maintain friendships, it's just as important to know when to let go and walk away. If you have a friend who makes you feel bad about yourself, is toxic, or brings you down, don't be afraid to walk away from the relationship. There is nothing wrong with letting go of someone who makes you unhappy.

Random Acts of Kindness

Being kind is one of the best ways to make and maintain friendships. Most people are drawn to kind people. Sometimes being kind comes naturally, but we can also develop this skill. Random acts of kindness are acts of kindness that you do for no reason. Not only do random acts of kindness make you feel good about yourself, but they also show others that you are a thoughtful and considerate person. Here are a few ideas on how to show random acts of kindness:

- Thank someone who you appreciate.

- Offer to help someone.

- Approach someone who is alone and invite them to join you.

- Give someone an honest compliment.

Dealing With Gossip

No matter how you look at it, gossiping about someone is wrong. If you're tempted to gossip, stop and think for a few seconds. Consider how it would feel if you were the subject of whatever it is you're about to say. Remember that it's never okay to say anything that isn't true. Even if the gossip is true, why take part in something that could hurt someone else's feelings and damage their reputation?

If you regularly gossip with your friends at school, others will eventually lose trust in you as a friend, which will jeopardize and damage your friendships. Remember that tables can turn. If you're involved in gossip, at some point, you may become the subject of gossip. Whenever you get the urge to talk about someone, pretend that they're standing right next to you. If you wouldn't say it to their face don't say it.

Below are four tips you can use to prevent gossip:

1. **Stop and change the subject.** As soon as someone starts to gossip, intentionally change the subject. Make it clear that you're not interested in hearing or participating in gossip.

2. **Defend the person.** Even if what is being said is true, defend the person in the most logical way possible. If you know that the gossip is a lie, call it that. If there is some truth to the gossip or you're not sure, say that you don't know the circumstances behind whatever it is being said, and that the person should be given the benefit of the doubt. Make it clear that you don't want to continue with the discussion.

3. **Don't rush to judgment.** When someone confides a piece of gossipy information about someone else, question it, and don't rush to judgment. Check the source. Don't believe something unless you have proof. The fact that most of your school is saying it does not constitute proof.

4. **Walk away.** If the gossip continues, walk away. The people gossiping will get the message that you don't approve of their behavior.

Always remind yourself that gossip can have a devastating effect on someone.

What may seem like harmless comments, fun banter, or a not-so-serious rumor can quickly snowball into something much bigger. Particularly cruel gossip could cause the person who is being talked about to develop mental health issues, such as depression. You don't want the guilt of having played a part in causing someone significant anguish and distress.

Learning To Accept Constructive Criticism

It's hard to take criticism without feeling hurt or getting defensive. After all, it often makes us feel attacked, uncomfortable, or less confident about ourselves. Many of us react with defensiveness and anger or, worse, may even lash out at the person who criticized us. But the truth is, there's value in constructive criticism. How else can we identify our weaknesses? When constructive criticism is valid and fair it can help us to improve our behavior.

Below are three ways to handle a situation in which you're on the receiving end of constructive criticism.

1. **Acknowledge any part of the criticism that's true**. Sometimes someone will make a general statement like, "you're <u>always</u> late" or "you <u>never</u> do your homework." When this happens, it helps to acknowledge that you sometimes engage in this behavior. For example, you could reply by saying, "I admit that there are times when I haven't done my homework." By owning up to the times or situations in which the person's criticism is true, you can focus on addressing what is going on right now.

2. **Own up to your mistakes.** When you mess up, even if unintentionally, the best thing to do is admit your mistake. For example, if you said something insensitive that hurt a friend's feelings, you could say, "I'm really sorry that what I said upset you. I'll try not to do it again."

3. **Ask for feedback.** A great way to learn from criticism is to ask the person to be clear about what they think you could improve. This information will allow you to get a better understanding of the other person's point of view. For example, if your

friend is offended by something you said, but you don't think you said anything offensive, you could say, "I am sorry that I upset you. Can you please explain what I said that upset you so that I can avoid upsetting you in the future?"

Work on re-framing the way you take feedback from others. Instead of getting offended or angry, ask yourself, "What am I meant to learn from this?" Don't beat yourself up about mistakes (we all make them). If you learn to process feedback differently and learn from it, you'll always bounce back stronger, wiser, and more resilient. Learning to accept positive criticism is easier to do if you remind yourself that constructive criticism is not an attack on you as a person. Instead, view it as an opportunity to become a better version of yourself.

> **LEARN TO SEE THE DIFFERENCE BETWEEN CONSTRUCTIVE AND DESTRUCTIVE CRITICISM. APPRECIATE THE CONSTRUCTIVE, IGNORE THE DESTRUCTIVE.**

Accepting Criticism Practice

Use the below activity to practice accepting constructive criticism.

Start by thinking of a time when someone gave you some constructive criticism. For example, a friend tells you that you always borrow her things and never return them.

What criticism did you receive?

_____

_____

_____

_____

How did you react to the criticism?

_____

_____

_____

_____

Regardless of how you have handled criticism in the past, use the charts on the following pages to identify how you could have responded to the feedback in a more positive and constructive way.

Skill	Appropriate Behavior	What I Could Have Said or Done
Acknowledge any part of the criticism that is true.	Try not to get defensive, angry or upset. Say that you'll try to make the change.	

Skill	Appropriate Behavior	What I Could Have Said or Done
Own up to your mistakes.	Don't blame someone else or make excuses. Acknowledge that you made a mistake.	

Skill	Appropriate Behavior	What I Could Have Said or Done
Ask for feedback.	Ask for advice on how you can improve. Ask yourself what you can learn from the criticism.	

Would the situation have gone differently if you had accepted the criticism and responded in the ways set out above. Would you have felt any different?

ACCEPT BOTH COMPLIMENTS AND CRITICISM. IT TAKES BOTH SUN AND RAIN FOR A FLOWER TO GROW.

The Power Of "I" Statements

Talking about sensitive and difficult topics with people we care about can be awkward. Sometimes we may feel unheard or misunderstood. The awesome thing about "I" statements is that they allow you to communicate your feelings and needs in a way that reduces blame and makes others less defensive. "You" statements can make the listener feel criticized, which will make them less open to engaging with you. "I" statements typically follow a set pattern beginning with "I" and how you feel. Follow this up by expressing what occurred that hurt your feelings. Finish by saying what it was about the behavior that hurt your feelings, and offer a preference or a solution.

Below are some examples:

- "I feel awful when you tease me about my shoes. It makes me feel like you don't care about my feelings. Could you please stop!"

- "I feel anxious when you call on me in class. It makes me feel like you are singling me out. I'd prefer it if you only called on me when I raise my hand."

- "I feel hurt when you don't keep your promise to sit next to me at lunch. When you ditch me for your other friends, it makes me feel like you don't value our friendship. I'd like it if you only make promises you intend to keep."

- "I feel sad when you don't stand up for me when Jasmine makes snide remarks about me. It makes me feel as if you don't have my back. I'd love it if you stood up for me."

Statement	Example
Blame:	"You're not pulling your weight on the group project."
"I" statement:	"I feel frustrated when you don't do the work you were assigned because I want to do well on this project."
Blame:	"I'm not lending you anything anymore because you never return them."
"I" statement:	"I feel angry when you don't return the pens you borrow because I need them for my art class."
Blame:	"I'm tired of you always gossiping about me behind my back."
"I" statement:	"I feel upset when I hear you've been gossiping about me behind my back because good friends don't do that."

"I" statement format: I feel _____ when you_____ because _____."

_____

_____

_____

_____

"I" Statements vs. "You" Statements

Read the statements in the table below and consider how you would react if these statements were said to you by a friend or family member. Consider how these statements would make them feel. Write down your thoughts in the middle column. In the last column, change the "You" statement to an "I" statement so that you minimize blame and clearly communicate what you mean.

"You" Statement	How Does It Make You Feel?	"I" Statement
You never listen to me.		
You're really annoying.		
You never believe me.		
Why do you always shout at me?		
You never take my side on anything!		
You always say mean things to me!		

Different Perspectives

In this activity, think about some recent social interactions that you've had. In the bubbles on the left, write down what you said. In the bubbles on the right, express how you think others may have perceived what you said. Were your words kind words, helpful words, or negative words? Did you ask questions? Did you stay on topic? How did you end the conversation?

What I Said	What Others May Have Perceived

BE PROUD OF WHO YOU ARE AND EVERYTHING YOU'VE OVERCOME.

Chapter 10

HOW TO DEAL WITH BULLYING

Chances are that you have already been on the receiving end of some sort of bullying. I was bullied at school throughout primary school and high school. At first, I blamed myself. In trying to make sense of it, I even started to convince myself that I must be unlikeable. But I eventually discovered that it's very common for students who are different to be bullied. This difference can be anything. You could be bullied for something as silly as being too tall or too short. Taylor Swift was bullied for liking country music. Lady Gaga was bullied for supposedly having a big nose. Millie Bobby Brown was bullied at school for being too pretty and confident.

Since being autistic makes us different, we make easy targets. Some studies have shown that up to 75% of autistic students report being bullied at school. In this chapter, I will share advice on how to deal with bullying. If you take away one message from this chapter, I want it to be that you are <u>not</u> to blame and are not alone. Don't ever forget that.

What's Bullying?

Bullying is a term that is commonly banded around and is used very liberally. So, I think I should give you the actual definition. **Bullying** is a deliberate act that is usually repeated and causes harm to someone else.

It can take different forms, such as verbal, physical, social, or psychological. Bullying can happen in person or online. It can be done by one person or by a group of people.

The four defining elements of bullying are that it's:

1. On purpose

2. Ongoing

3. Harmful / Upsetting

4. An imbalance and abuse of power

There are four main types of school bullying, each of which is discussed below:

- **Physical bullying.** This kind of bullying includes a range of aggressive behaviors in which one person aims to cause bodily harm to another person. Examples of physical bullying include: hitting, kicking, pushing, and tripping.

- **Verbal bullying.** Although you may have been told that "words will never hurt you," anyone who has been on the receiving end of verbal bullying knows that cruel words and scary threats can be very hurtful. Examples of verbal bullying include name-calling, insults, teasing, and taunting.

- **Relational bullying.** In relational bullying, young people use friendship or the threat of taking their friendship away to hurt others. This is the type of bullying that is often referred to as "drama." Because it usually happens within the context of a once trusting friendship, relational bullying can be especially hurtful and confusing.

Examples of relational bullying include: starting hurtful rumors, excluding and ostracizing the person, giving them the silent treatment, gossiping about them, and following up a purposely cruel statement with "just joking" or "don't be so sensitive."

- **Cyberbullying.** Cyberbullying is a specific form of bullying that involves technology. Cyberbullying can be incredibly destructive because of how quickly and how widely hateful messages can spread. Examples of cyberbullying include: mocking someone online, posting embarrassing photos online, harassing someone on social media, making fun of someone in a group chat, and setting up fake social media accounts to hurt someone and damage their reputation.

THE WAY THAT PEOPLE TREAT YOU SAYS A LOT MORE ABOUT THEM THAN IT DOES ABOUT YOU.

What Does Bullying Look Like?

As previously mentioned, bullying can take many forms. Some common examples of bullying behavior include:

- Talking badly about someone behind their back (online or in-person).

- Teasing someone, calling them names, giving them nasty looks, or making rude gestures.

- Spreading rumors or lies about someone (online or in-person).

- Hurting someone physically by pushing, hitting, slapping or restraining them.

- Excluding someone from a group (online or in-person).

- Harassing someone because of their race, sex, religion, gender, or a disability.

- Sharing embarrassing photos of someone online.

- Posting mean things about someone on social media.

- Harassing someone online with negative comments.

Sometimes it can be difficult to identify bullying behavior, especially when it's subtle, and you're the victim. You may find that you second guess yourself, try to justify the action, or that others disagree that you're being bullied. This is especially true when a person says something mean and follows it up with "I was just kidding."

Below are some examples of bullying that are particularly applicable to autistic people:

- **Take advantage of your sensory sensitivities.** Physical bullying doesn't have to involve actual contact. A bully can inflict physical discomfort in subtler ways, such as invading your personal space on a continual and relentless basis or deliberately causing you sensory pain. For example, if the bully knows you're autistic and sensitive to noise and lights and deliberately makes loud noises to cause you discomfort and pain, their actions constitute bullying.

- **Criticize you based on your autism or another disability.** A bully may draw on existing stereotypes and misconceptions to make disparaging remarks about your autism. This may make you feel embarrassed, ashamed, isolated, and alone. It's never acceptable to say something derogatory, cruel, or offensive, especially about someone with a disability.

- **Treat you differently in a group or in front of others.** The bully may treat you differently when you are in a group or in front of others by singling you out. I had a so-called friend who would discuss plans to go to the mall, and then turn to me and say that I wasn't invited. This supposed friend also cropped me out of all her Instagram posts. A person who goes out of their way to exclude you, who puts you down or makes fun of you in front of others is a bully.

- **Set you up.** Sometimes bullies will try to get you in trouble by setting you up. This can jeopardize your relationships with your teachers and can cause you setbacks at school. If you're academic, the bully may be motivated by jealousy and may want to sabotage you by limiting your progress and preventing you from succeeding.

If you're questioning or doubting whether you're being bullied, listen to your body. Your body will often respond to bullying in psychosomatic ways, which is a physical illness that occurs due to mental trauma or stress. I started suffering from crippling stomach aches, insomnia and even began having panic attacks. You may have an overwhelming feeling of nausea, anxiety, or stress when you're in the presence of the bully, or may experience more physical symptoms like throwing up, a rapid heartbeat, headaches, and panic attacks. For example, on the way to school, you may feel physically ill at the thought of having to see the bully.

Don't ignore these signs. Your body is trying to tell you that the bullying is affecting your wellbeing.

SOME DAYS YOU HAVE TO CREATE YOUR OWN SUNSHINE.

What To Do If You're Being Bullied

Being bullied can turn your world upside. It can make you feel scared, anxious, ashamed, lonely, and rejected. You may feel helpless and feel like there's nothing you can do to make it stop. You may even begin to blame yourself. I know I did. To make matters worse, sometimes people witness the bullying and don't do anything to help you. These passive bystanders may even be your friends.

Bullying can be really confusing. You might not even realize that it's happening to you at first. It may start off as something fairly innocent like a joke that gradually escalates out of control. Or perhaps it's more physical, like someone at school shoving you whenever they walk past.

It's important to remember that being bullied is **not** your fault. There's nothing wrong with you. You did not do anything to deserve it. Don't ever blame yourself. As someone who has lots of experience of being bullied, I promise you that no matter how awful and bleak the situation may feel like, you have the strength to get through it. Below are some steps that you can take that will allow you to regain control of your life.

If you are being bullied face-to-face, try following these steps:

- **Ignore it.** One way to respond to bullying is to ignore it and calmly walk away. Try not to give the bully or people bullying you the satisfaction of a reaction. Sometimes bullying will stop if you don't react. In many cases, bullies feed off your response. If you get angry or visibly upset by their actions, they may continue doing it. On the other hand, if you ignore it, they may get bored and stop.

- **Talk it out.** If you're feeling incredibly brave, consider telling the person or people who are bullying you to stop. This may be enough to end the bullying. There's a chance that they don't realize they're doing it, or that they don't know how much it's hurting you.

- **Don't fight back.** Don't ever retaliate or fight back. Don't sink to their level. If you fight back, you could make the situation much worse. You could get hurt or be blamed for starting the fight. Instead, always walk away.

- **Avoid the person who is bullying you.** Try to avoid the places where your bully hangs out. Identify the areas where the bully is more likely to approach you, such as stairways and hallways. If you can't avoid these places, try to plan it so that there are teachers or adults around when you are there.

- **Try not to be alone.** Bullies usually select their victims based on how easy they think it will be to bully them. People who are alone are more vulnerable and can be appealing targets for bullies. When you're at school, try to always be around teachers and other adults or around friends. Bullies feel empowered to bully one person, but they will rarely bully a group. Ask your friends to stay with you while the bully is around. This way, you're less of an easy target, and you have backup if the bully starts being nasty.

- **Tell a trusted adult.** Sometimes it can be helpful to speak to an adult that you trust. Telling an adult can help you find ways to get the bullying to stop and help you overcome the negative feelings that can result from being bullying. You could tell a parent, teacher, or a relative. It's useful to keep a list of the things the bully has said or done, including specific details about each incident like the dates, times and locations. This evidence will make it easier to explain the severity, and frequency of the bullying. It may seem daunting to tell an adult about the bullying, especially since it can feel like you're being a tattletale. But remember that asking for help when you need it is a really brave and mature thing to do.

Bullies like to isolate their victims by making them feel alone and helpless and shaming them into silence. Confiding in someone will mean that you're no longer alone, may get useful advice on how to stop the bullying, and will be better equipped to stop the bullying.

What To Do If You're Being Cyber-Bullied

If you're being bullied online, here are some steps that you can take:

- **Report any bullying to the site where it's occurring.** All social media platforms have a reporting system. It's anonymous, straightforward, and depending on what you've reported; there's a chance it could get taken down quickly.

- **Keep copies of everything that's sent to you.** Take screenshots of everything that is sent to you, whether they're nasty comments, pictures, or messages. Having a permanent copy of abusive messages will provide you with evidence to show others and help you prove that you're being cyber-bullied.

- **Block, block, block.** Block the person or people from being able to contact you. Change your privacy settings and passwords so that you can protect what you post on social media.

- **Delete your current online account, and start a new one.** If the bullying is persistent and ongoing, delete your account and create a new one. Only give your new details to a few of your most trusted friends.

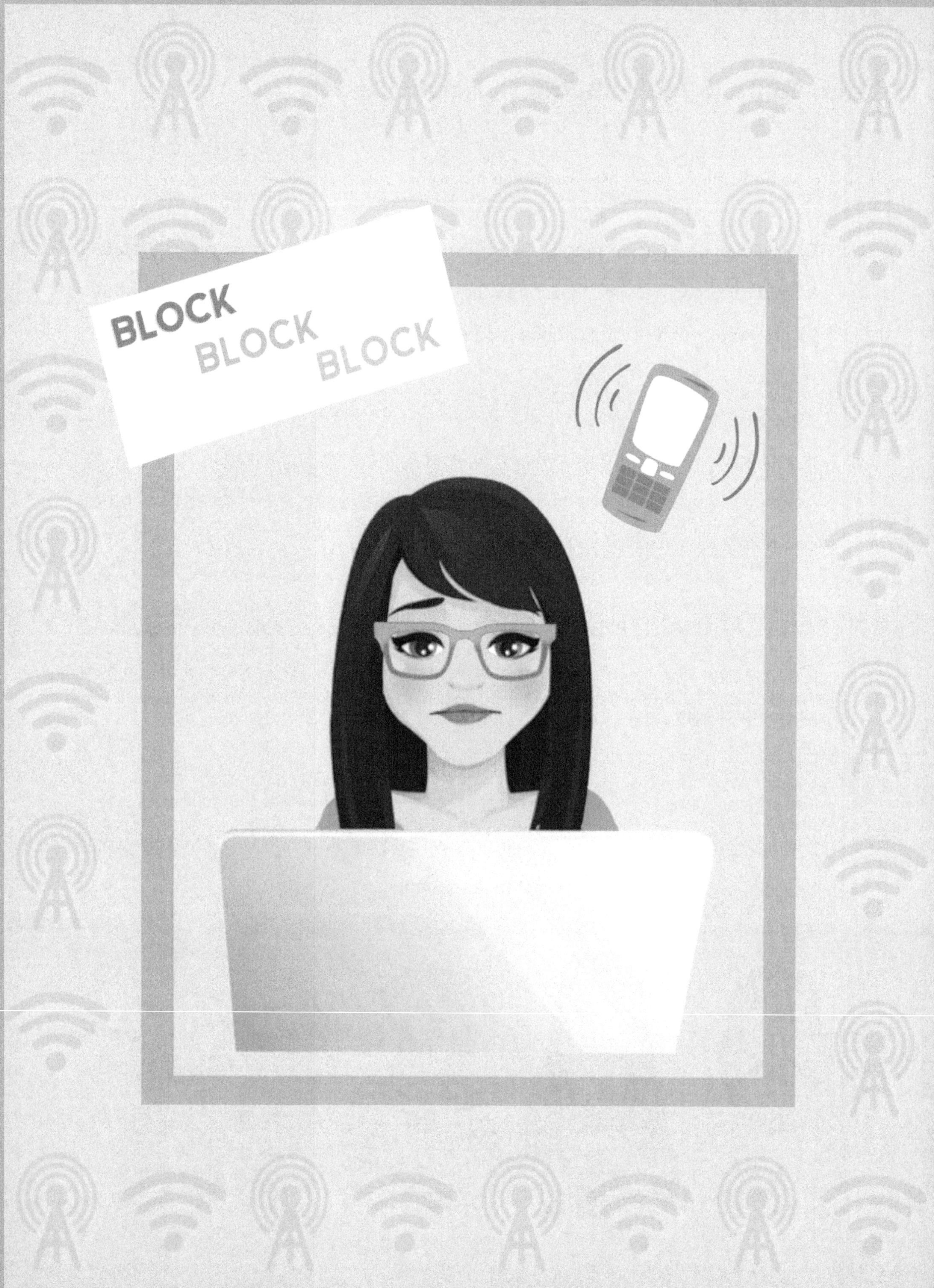
BLOCK
BLOCK
BLOCK

Who's A Bystander?

Someone who sees or knows that bullying is taking place but does nothing to prevent it is called a **bystander**. A bystander can have a huge impact on someone who is being bullied by being an **upstander**, someone who speaks out when they see that someone is being bullied. It can be scary to step in when you witness someone being bullied. For one thing, confronting someone about their behavior is never easy. You may also worry that speaking up will make you the bully's next target. But I also know that when I was being bullied, it would've made a world of difference if someone had spoken up and stood up for me. It would've have made me feel less isolated and alone.

What Can I Do If I'm A Bystander?

If you observe someone bullying someone else, try not to support the bullying by looking on and doing nothing, laughing at the person being bullied, or liking or sharing hurtful photos or posts online. This makes you complicit in the abuse.

If it's safe to do so, step in and speak up in an assertive but non-aggressive way. If you don't feel it's safe to step in, report what you observed to a trusted adult. Show the person being bullied that you're there for them by helping them to walk away from the situation. Remind the person being bullied that it's not their fault and there is always help available.

Don't stand by!

Stand up.
Stand strong.
Don't tolerate bullying.

Top 10 Tips For Dealing with Being Bullied

Here are some tips that can help you if you're being bullied:

1	Talk to someone. Don't suffer in silence.
2	Do not retaliate or fight back directly against a bully. Walk away.
3	If you're being bullied by your friends, cut your losses and find new friends.
4	Try not to give the bully the satisfaction of a reaction.
5	Try to avoid and not be alone with the bully.
6	Ask your friends to tell the bully that their behavior is unacceptable.
7	If you witness someone physically bullying someone immediately tell an adult.
8	Try to be an upstander.
9	Document. Document. Document.
10	Remember, bullying isn't your fault.

Famous People Who Were Bullied

Did you know that many of today's most successful celebrities were bullied at school?

Check out the stars below.

Zendaya

Zendaya believes her childhood bullying toughened her up and made her better equipped to deal with life in the spotlight.

Rihanna

Rihanna was bullied in school for her skin color. However, she now says she's grateful because the experience made her stronger.

Taylor Swift

Taylor was bullied for liking country music. Her bullies gave her inspiration to start writing songs.

Jennifer Lawrence

Jennifer has said that her bullying became so bad that she switched schools to get away from the mean girls.

Jessica Alba

"I'd eat my lunch in the nurses' office so I didn't have to sit with the other girls. I'd get beaten up and picked on all the time. It was about being different and not fitting in."

Shay Mitchell

"Instead of eating lunch in the cafeteria, I'd find the quietest place at school and eat by myself. I realized that bullying never has to do with you. It's the bully who's insecure."

Millie Bobby Brown

"I was bullied by a group of students. I remember feeling helpless. School used to be a safe place and now I was scared to go. I didn't know who I could trust."

Lady Gaga

"I was teased for being ugly, having a big nose, being annoying. Your laugh is funny. You're weird. Why do you do your makeup that way?"

Getting Support

The most important thing to keep in mind when you're being bullied is that you don't have to go through it alone. Don't stay silent. Keeping it to yourself can mean that the bullying escalates and that it begins to affect your mental health. You have people who care about you who will want to help.

You may feel so bad that you start having harmful or suicidal thoughts. If this happens to you, make sure that you reach out to a parent, a friend, a teacher, or a trusted adult. If you want to speak to someone anonymously, contact a suicide hotline or charity. They'll help to support you so that you can get through this experience. If you don't feel like speaking to someone, you can find lots of help online.

Below are some useful websites that you may find help.

- www.pacerteensagainstbullying.org

- www.stompoutbullying.org

- www.bornthisway.foundation

- www.kindcampaign.com

- www.loveislouder.org

- www.itgetsbetter.org

- www.napab.org

- www.stopbullying.gov/resources/kids

WHEN LIFE CHANGES ITSELF TO HARDER, CHANGE YOURSELF TO STRONGER.

KINDNESS IS

PULLING

SOMEONE UP

AFTER THEY'VE

BEEN KNOCKED

DOWN.

YOUR STRUGGLES
DEVELOP YOUR
STRENGTHS. WHEN
YOU GO THROUGH
HARDSHIP AND
ADVERSITY, AND
REFUSE TO GIVE UP,
THAT IS STRENGTH.

Chapter 11

RECOGNIZING YOUR STRENGTHS

Recognizing Your Strengths

Everyone has their own set of strengths and weaknesses. Think of something that you want to improve about yourself. Is it a strength or a weakness? It's very likely that you thought of a weakness. Most people tend to believe that we should prioritize improving our weaknesses over improving our strengths. As a result, we often have a poor sense of our own strengths and talents. At school, much more emphasis is placed on improving your weak areas than on nurturing and enhancing our strengths. Eventually, most of us become experts at focusing on our weaknesses. This mindset is why some of our strengths remain dormant or are neglected. However, studies have shown that we benefit more from developing our strengths than from improving our weaknesses. While understanding and working on our weaknesses is important, developing our strengths makes us happier, less stressed, and more confident. On the other hand, focusing on our weaknesses can be demoralizing and make you feel that you're not good enough.

If you're finding that you're failing to meet your goals, it may be time to consider trying to improve your strengths, rather than focusing all of your efforts on getting better in the areas where you're weak.

If you're not sure what your strengths are, don't worry. This chapter will give you some tips on how to find them.

How To Find Your Strengths

Finding your strengths can be tricky. Weaknesses are often glaringly obvious. They evoke vivid memories. For example, I still cringe at the thought of being last in every Sports Day event. On the other hand, most of us take our talents for granted. Sometimes our strengths come so naturally and effortlessly to us that we aren't even aware of them. We assume everyone else is just as capable. Failing to acknowledge our strengths can prevent us from developing them.

We tend to think of strengths as things that we're good at and weaknesses as things that we're bad at. This overgeneralization doesn't take into consideration that strengths can be disguised as weaknesses. For example, sometimes a trait or characteristic that you may get in trouble for is actually a strength. For example, if you've been told you're bossy, you could be a natural leader. If you're often accused of being a tattletale, you may have a strong sense of justice and could excel in a career in law.

Does it energize you? I have found that one useful way to find your strengths is to identify the things that energize, excite, and invigorate you. Strengths make you feel good and positive about yourself, whereas weaknesses make you feel like you're not good enough.

Think about how certain activities make you feel. An activity could be a strength if:

- It makes you feel positive and successful.

- You're naturally drawn to it, even if you don't know why.

- You can spend hours on the activity without getting bored or tired.

Ask your family and friends. Although you may find it hard to see your own strengths, your family and friends will be able to tell you. Ask your parents, siblings, and friends for their insight into where they think your strengths lie. Keep in mind that some people may respond in a way that's unhelpful. For example, your parents may tell you that you're good at everything. That's okay. The goal is to discover strengths that you wouldn't have identified on your own or to find patterns of strengths. Once you have your answers, analyze the responses. Do any of the strengths they mentioned excite or energize you? If so, these may be strengths you want to grow.

What are your proudest accomplishments? Another way to find your strengths is to think of your proudest accomplishments. Look at these accomplishments and try to determine what each says about you. For example, your proudest accomplishments may be winning an art competition, creating personalized cards, and teaching yourself photography and how to use Photoshop. The common thread that ties these activities together is that they are all a form of art. By looking at your proudest accomplishments and for a common theme, you may get some insight into your strengths, particularly if these strengths match up with what others have told you.

After you've identified your strengths, the next step is to create a plan for how you'll develop and nurture these strengths. If the strengths you found were things you haven't focused on before, your first step may be as simple as starting to learn more about your newfound strength. You can start by joining a school club, reading books on the subject, or looking for online tutorials.

Identifying Your Strengths

Now that you have spent some time identifying your strengths look at the following list of strengths and circle all of the strengths that apply to you.

Accurate	Fair	Insightful	Persuasive
Adaptable	Flexible	Inspirational	Practical
Adventurous	Focused	Intelligent	Precise
Artistic	Friendly	Jovial	Problem-solver
Attentive	Funny	Judicious	Responsible
Bold	Generous	Lively	Resourceful
Brave	Genuine	Logical	Sensible
Caring	Giving	Loyal	Serious
Clever	Grateful	Mature	Sincere
Charming	Gracious	Mindful	Straightforward
Confident	Gutsy	Motivated	Tenacious
Considerate	Hard-working	Observant	Thorough
Critical-thinker	Helpful	Open-minded	Thoughtful
Curious	Honest	Optimistic	Tolerant
Dependable	Hopeful	Organized	Trustworthy
Determined	Humble	Outgoing	Truthful
Eager	Imaginative	Passionate	Unique
Easy-going	Impassioned	Patient	Voracious
Eloquent	Independent	Perceptive	Wise
Enthusiastic	Industrious	Persistant	Witty

Uncovering Your Strengths

The following questions will help you to uncover your strengths.

What's something that you can do effortlessly that others find hard?

_____

_____

_____

What do others often ask you to help them with?

_____

_____

_____

Think of a time when you successfully overcame a challenge or setback. What skills did you use to help you to overcome this challenge?

_____

_____

_____

_____

What are you best at in school? What characteristics make you successful in this area?

_____

_____

_____

_____

Think about the things that you love to do the most. What is it about these activities that you love? Is there a common theme?

_____

_____

_____

_____

Ask your parents, family or friends to tell you some of your strengths?

_____

_____

_____

_____

_____

I Am ....

Identify which of the strengths included in the table below are true, semi-true, and not true.

Take a moment to focus on all your strengths.

	True		
I am ambitious.			
I am artistic.			
I am athletic.			
I am brave.			
I am caring.			
I am considerate.			
I am confident.			
I am curious			
I am determined.			
I am enthusiastic.			
I am focused.			
I am generous.			
I am hard-working.			
I am imaginative.			
I am kind.			
I am a problem-solver.			

My Strength Stories

Now that you have identified some of your strengths select two of your strengths. For each one, think of a time when you displayed this characteristic and answer the following questions.

Strength #1: _____

When and how did you display this strength?

_____

_____

_____

Strength #2: _____

When and how did you display this strength?

_____

_____

_____

Using Your Strengths

People who identify and apply their strengths are more likely to succeed in achieving their goals. These people are also happier, less stressed, and more confident. This activity will help you to think about how you can harness your unique strengths and talents.

My top five strengths are:

1. _____

2. _____

3. _____

4. _____

5. _____

Describe a time when you used your strength to achieve your goal, to help someone solve a problem or to make a positive difference.

_____

_____

_____

_____

_____

_____

From Failure To Success

Below is a list of famous women who failed before they succeeded. Never forget that with hard work, patience, and perseverance you can achieve your goals. It's also important to remember that most of our successes are built on our failures. As the success stories of these celebrities show, failures are stepping stones to our success.

Millie Bobby Brown

Millie had so many rejections that she nearly gave up acting before she landed the part of Eleven in Stranger Things.

Lady Gaga

Lady Gaga was dropped by her first record label, after three months. She's since won six Grammy awards!

Oprah Winfrey

Oprah was fired from her first TV job as an anchor for getting too emotionally invested in her stories.

J.K. Rowling

J.K. Rowling was a single, mom on government benefits when she wrote the first Harry Potter book.

Be Motivated By Setbacks

Most people get upset when they fail at something. It's natural to feel frustrated, disappointed, or even angry. This is especially true if you tried really hard to succeed. I've learned to reframe failure so that I now view it as part of the journey towards success. For example, let's say you wanted to get the lead in your school play, but it was given to someone else. You could chose to be so discouraged by this setback that you decide to never audition for another play. Or you could use the disappointment as motivation. It could fuel your determination to get a lead role in your school's next play. You could increase your chances by practicing more and by asking your drama teacher to give you advice on how to improve. You could also watch videos on how to improve your technique, and so on. In other words, you could use your failure as an opportunity to set you up for future success.

Can you think of a time when you failed at something, but then were able to finally achieve it? Write about it below.

My Battle Cry!

Come up with a battle cry to help you feel strong and empowered. When I feel uncertain or lack confidence in myself, I tell myself to never give up because small achievements eventually add up to huge results.

My Trophy Collection

On this page, give yourself credit for all your accomplishments, no matter how large or small.

When I have setbacks, I don't give up.

Celebrate Strengths

My Strengths

Mirror, Mirror

Write encouraging messages to yourself on the mirrors below. Don't be afraid to give yourself a compliment.

I'm capable of amazing things.

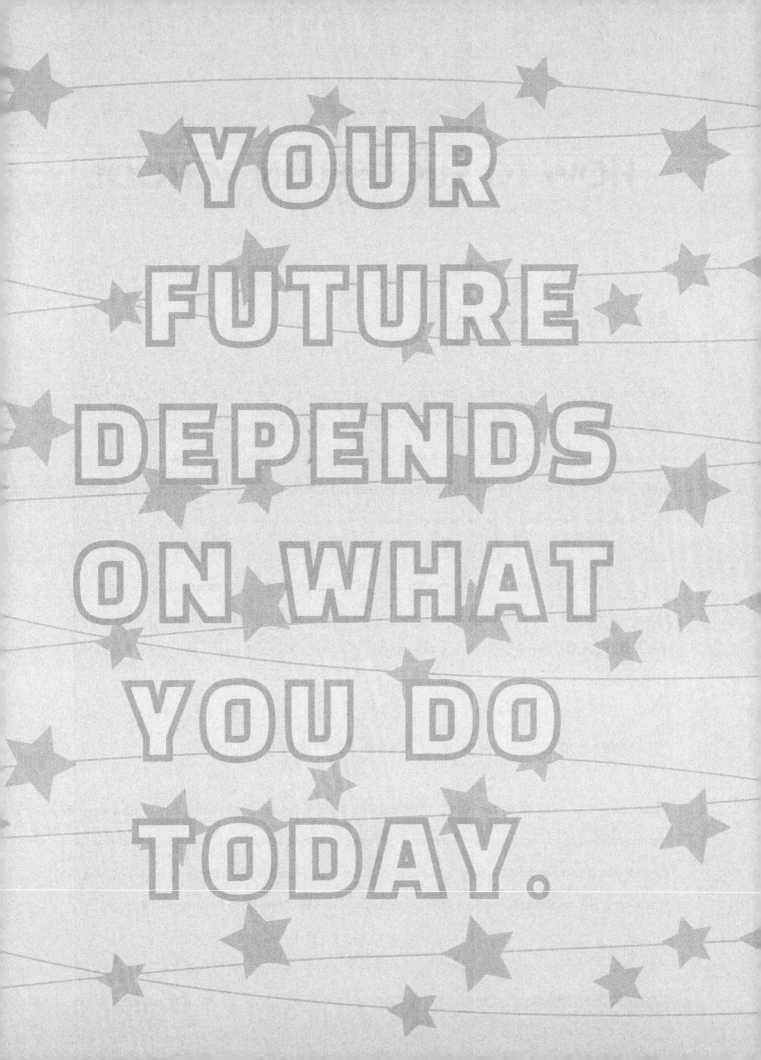

Chapter 12

HOW TO SUCCEED IN SCHOOL

Succeeding In School

Succeeding in school can be challenging if you're autistic. Most schools don't cater to the needs of their autistic students; instead, we're expected to adapt and assimilate into the school environment. An environment that isn't designed for people who are autistic. It's incredibly hard to learn in a classroom environment where the lights are too bright, it's too loud, and too crowded. Where sensory sensitivities make it impossible to focus and learn.

Many autistic individuals also have a learning difference, that can make succeeding in school even more challenging. In my case, in addition to being autistic, I also have dyslexia, dyspraxia (DCD), and ADHD. These conditions made it difficult to succeed in school. It didn't help that many of my teachers had no clue how to support and teach students with learning differences. It also didn't help that most of my teachers didn't understand or recognize how hard I was trying and that some of my teachers were really mean.

Although I had a bumpy start and it took a while to find my stride, I eventually found ways to compensate for my sensory and learning difference challenges. In this chapter, I will share all the tips and tricks that I used to succeed in school, including helping you to identify your learning style, organizational and time management tips, and how to stay motivated.

What Is Executive Function?

Do you have a hard time keeping track of your belongings? Have you ever gone to your bedroom to fetch something and then forgotten what it was you wanted to get? Do you have trouble keeping track of time? All of these examples rely on executive function skills. **Executive function** is the ability to plan, focus, remember instructions, and juggle multiple tasks successfully. Just as an air traffic control system at a busy airport safely manages many aircraft arrivals and departures on numerous runways, our brain does something similar. Our executive function allows us to filter distractions, prioritize tasks, set and achieve goals, and control impulses.

Many autistic individuals have poor executive function. Someone with executive functioning problems may struggle with planning, following multi-step instructions, organization, time management, setting schedules, and completing tasks. For example, I used to frequently misplace my school books, homework, my sports kit, and even my school backpack. I was a hot mess! I seemed to be incapable of keeping track of my belongings. If this description could be describing you, don't worry, I can help by sharing my strategies.

If you are uncertain whether you could benefit from improving your executive function, here are some examples:

- You're always misplacing your school books.

- You frequently forget to take important items back and forth form school.

- You frequently forget to go to your lunch club or after school club.

- You frequently underestimate the amount of time it takes to do your homework.

- You struggle to juggle and identify which homework to prioritize.

- You get so overwhelmed by your homework assignments that you don't know where to begin.

- You struggle to organize and structure you writing and to pick out the important information when reading a passage.

- You struggle to retell events chronologically.

- You struggle to recall and follow multi-step instructions.

- You frequently lose your keys, as well as other essential items and belongings that you care about.

What Type Of Learner Am I?

One of the keys to succeeding in school is using a studying method that suits your learning style. We all learn differently. Not every study strategy, such as using flashcards or taking thorough notes, is best for every type of learner. It's essential to identify your learning style so that you can tailor your studying to suit your needs. Many people learn best through a combination of different learning styles, so multiple styles may appeal to you.

Here are some of the most common learning styles and some tips for studying.

Visual learners. If you're a visual learner, the best way to learn is by using images, pictures, and spatial understanding. Instead of studying by reading pages and pages of notes, try converting your notes into mind maps, flow charts, drawings, infographics and diagrams. You are also likely to benefit from having color-coded notes. Your pencil case should include lots of different-colored highlighters, pens, and post-it notes.

Auditory learners. If you're an auditory learner, the best way for you to learn is by listening. Ask your teachers if you can be allowed to record your lessons so that you can listen to them later. If this is not an option, I suggest that you focus all your attention on what your teacher is saying instead of simultaneously taking notes. When studying for a test, try repeating the information to yourself. For example, record yourself reading the relevant parts of the textbook and repeatedly listen to the recording. If you're an auditory learner, you will benefit from listening to Khan Academy lectures, switching to audiobooks, and writing essays using text-to-speech technology.

Physical or kinesthetic learners. If you're a kinesthetic learner, the best way to learn is by using your body, hands, and sense of touch. You will learn best by incorporating movement into your studying. Try memorizing your notes while standing, walking, or moving around. Some people find it helps them to learn and retain the information. When you are at school, incorporate small discreet movements that won't distract others. For example, twisting a rubber band around a pencil while you listen to your teacher or read. When preparing for a test, you're likely to benefit from creating physical flashcards that you can touch and flip or by using interactive apps like Quizlet.

Three-Step Planning

Do you always put things off? I'm guilty of doing this. Unfortunately, this approach never works. Just because we choose to ignore the task doesn't make it go away. The history essay still has to be written. The math problems still have to be solved. The homework still has to be done no matter how much you procrastinate. So if you often leave things to the last minute, below are some tips that may help you.

Start by asking yourself what is causing your procrastination. Once you know the cause, it will be easier to tackle. For example, if you're afraid that you won't be able to do the task as well as you'd like, you can tell yourself that even if you make a mistake, it's not the end of the world, and what matters is that you tried your best.

If you feel overwhelmed by the magnitude of the task and don't know where or how to begin, it helps to simplify and break down the task so that it becomes much more manageable. I suggest you take the following three steps:

1. **Come up with an idea, goal, or plan.** For example, your goal may be that you want to improve your grades.

2. **Take the goal and break it into smaller goals.** To improve your grades, you could study more regularly, ask for help, identify the areas you need to improve, and regularly read your class notes.

3. **Now break those goals into even smaller steps.** You could set aside a specific time every day to study. You could identify someone who may be able to help you, such as a teacher or classmate. You could create a list of the

areas you need to study and focus on strengthening these areas. You could resolve to read through your class notes each evening.

The key to achieving your goal is to break it down into small pieces so that it doesn't feel too intimidating and too big to conquer. Here are some additional strategies that you may also find helpful.

- Set concrete deadlines for yourself.

- Eliminate distractions from your environment.

- Get yourself started by committing to work for only 5 minutes.

- Reward yourself for your accomplishments.

- Avoid a perfectionist mindset.

- Focus on your goals instead of on your tasks.

- Visualize your future self turning in the homework.

THE GREATEST WASTE OF TIME IS THE TIME SPENT NOT GETTING STARTED.

Finding Your Motivation

It's hard to be motivated when it comes to a task you don't like. I really disliked French and dreaded having to study for it. Every time I sat down to do my French homework, I would have to fight the urge to do almost anything else instead. Even cleaning my room and rearranging my sock draw was more appealing! If you find it hard to get motivated to do something you dislike, try one of the following hacks.

Set a starter timer. Sometimes, the hardest part of tackling a task is getting started. The dread of having to do something you aren't motivated to do is often worse than actually doing it. Once you start, you'll find it wasn't as bad as you thought. If you can't motivate yourself to begin a task, set a timer for 5 minutes. Tell yourself that once those 5 minutes are up, you will commit to getting the task done.

Cover it up. If you feel overwhelmed by having to do a lot of work, use a piece of paper (I like to use pastel-colored paper) to cover the questions you aren't working on. For example, if you have to write four essays, cover the essay questions you're not working on. By visually blocking out these questions, you can focus on one essay at a time. I find that this strategy makes the task much more manageable.

Pair a like with a dislike. If you particularly dislike a specific type of homework, forcing yourself to do it can seem like torture. To make the experience less unpleasant, try pairing the homework you don't like with something you enjoy. For example, if you dislike doing your chemistry homework try jazzing it up by doing the homework outdoors, while listening to music in the background, or while burning a favorite scented candle. I find that pairing a negative with a positive can really help.

Promise yourself a reward. One way to motivate yourself is to give yourself a small treat so that you have something to look forward to. Before you take on an unpleasant task, get a sticky note, and write down a small reward you can treat yourself to after finishing the task. Ideas could include having a favorite snack (chocolate always works for me), spending 10 minutes on TikTok, or watching an episode of your favorite show. Place the sticky note somewhere you can see it so that it incentivizes you to keep going.

Visualize your future self thanking you. Take a second to visualize and imagine how happy, relieved, and accomplished, you will feel after you have completed the task. Use this feeling to motivate you to keep going.

Setting Goals

Do you have a hard time getting started with your homework? Whether you have to write an essay, solve some algebra problems, or study for your biology quiz, I find that it helps to set a realistic goal. Before you sit down to do your homework, write a realistic goal that you want to achieve during that study session. The key is to make the goal achievable within your timeframe. So instead of "write my Romeo and Juliet essay," an achievable goal may be to "plan the essay and draft the introductory paragraph." Or instead of "finish algebra homework," you could write "complete five algebra problems on the worksheet."

This approach will help you manage your time better and make the task much less daunting. Let's practice this approach.

> **Kayla has set aside 2 hours in 30-minute chunks this evening to do her homework. She has a lot to do, including writing an English paper and studying for a Spanish quiz. She is having trouble knowing where to begin and is feeling overwhelmed. She'd like to break down her tasks into smaller, more specific, and attainable goals but doesn't know where to start.**

In the chart on the following page, write a smaller, more specific goal that corresponds to the larger task. For example, since Kayla has the big task of studying for a Spanish quiz, a smaller goal could be for her to memorize twenty Spanish vocabulary words.

Big Task	Smaller, More Specific Task
Write an essay on Lord of the Flies that is due in two weeks.	Create an outline. Draft the introductory paragraph.
Study for Spanish vocabulary quiz that covers 50 words.	
Create a timeline of the causes of World War II for history class.	
Create a poster explaining photosynthesis for biology class.	

STAY POSITIVE.

WORK HARD.

MAKE IT HAPPEN.

Focus
on the goal
and not on
the obstacles.

Awesome Study Techniques

Have you ever spent hours studying only to realize you haven't learned anything? One of the keys to succeeding in school is to study efficiently and effectively.

Here are some study techniques that will help you to retain information when you are studying.

Use notecards. Create flashcards with vocabulary words, dates, or other information that you need to memorize. I suggest you create two different categories. If you're consistently correctly answering a flashcard, put it into a separate "review" flashcard pile. This strategy allows you to identify and focus on the information that you need to prioritize.

Use sticky notes. Write vocabulary words, dates, or other information that you need to memorize on sticky notes and stick them <u>everywhere</u>. I attach the notes on my bathroom mirror, my bedside table, and my computer screen. Reading the notes repeatedly throughout the day will help to reinforce the information you're trying to learn.

Color-code your notes. Color-coding your notes can highlight and prioritize important information, help you organize the material logically, and make your study time more productive. Whether you use purple for main ideas, green for action items, or blue for facts and figures, always use the same colors throughout your notes to represent the same categories of information. You may find it helpful to keep a table in the front of your notebook with a list of your categories of information and their corresponding colors. Try to use the same system for all of your classes to avoid confusion. Eventually, the meanings of the individual colors will become second nature to you.

A word of warning about color-coding your notes. It can be tempting to highlight everything, which will be counter-productive. Try to limit your use of color-coding to the most critical information. If everything is highlighted, nothing will stand out as important. Think of color-coding as being like road signs: If there were too many road signs, you'd be overwhelmed with too much information, and you may even get lost. In the same way, too much color-coding can be distracting and can lead to information overload. Remember that the goal of color-coding is to focus your attention and make your notes clearer and easier to navigate. Every color should serve a specific purpose and point you in the right direction.

Quiz yourself. One strategy that I find useful is to think about the types of questions I may be asked on a test. I then design my own mock test with the types of questions and concepts that I think I will be asked. This strategy allows me to focus my study sessions on answering these questions.

Paraphrase and reflect. How many times have you read a few paragraphs in a textbook only to realize that you didn't retain a single concept or key point? This used to happen to me all the time. One strategy I use to ensure I retain the information I read is to write one or two sentences paraphrasing the concept or key point. I imagine that I am explaining the content to a five-year old. Having to summarize the information and explain the content in basic and simple terms forces you to understand the informations.

Conquering Time Management

Many autistic people struggle with time management. **Time management** is a skill that helps you to:

- Make a good guess at how long it will take to do something.

- Complete tasks on time.

- Use your time efficiently.

If you have a hard time juggling your homework, chores, and other commitments, you may need to work on your time management skills.

Here are some strategies that you can use to manage your time more efficiently:

- **Identify your priorities.** Prioritize your commitments by deciding which task is most important and should be completed first. For example, if your art project is due tomorrow, work on this first.

- **Time your homework.** By timing how long it takes you to complete different types of homework, you'll have an idea of how much time to allot for each task. For example, you may need a lot more time to write an English essay than you may need to do your biology homework.

- **Keep track of time.** Use your smartphone, alarm clock, or watch to give you regular reminders every 15 or 30 minutes when you're working on a task. This approach will ensure that you don't lose track of time and have enough time to work on another homework assignment or commitment.

Don't forget to build in breaks when you're studying. Although dedicating three nonstop hours to one task may seem like the best way to approach an urgent task, studies have shown that this can be counterproductive. Instead, building in study breaks will give you the mental rest you need to refocus, see the big picture, and jump back into your studying with renewed energy.

Make a to-do list and put it in order of priority so you do the urgent task first.

Don't forget to take frequent study breaks.

Don't leave tasks until the last minute. Your future self will thank you for it.

Harness Your Hyperfocus

Have you ever been so absorbed in an activity that you became oblivious to everything that was going on around you? Some autistic individuals, in particular those who also have ADHD, have the ability to hyperfocus. **Hyperfocus** is the deep and intense focus on one single activity. When you hyperfocus, you may lose track of the passage of time and forget about your other chores and responsibilities.

The downside of being able to hyperfocus is that you may have difficulty focusing on tasks you find boring. You may also become so engaged in activities that you're passionate that you don't do your homework. For example, instead of completing your chemistry homework that's due tomorrow, you may spend hours reading about climate change. Although your hyperfocus can negatively affect your life by distracting you from completing important tasks, it can also be harnessed to your advantage.

Here are some strategies that I use to take advantage of my hyperfocus.

Get to know your hyperfocus. Keep track of the situations and activities that cause you to hyperfocus. There may be times when you aren't aware that you are hyperfocusing. By writing down each time you hyperfocus, you will begin to identify what types of activities will cause you to hyperfocus. You may be able to identify patterns and trends that you can use to your advantage.

Practice controlling your hyperfocus. Use the tasks and activities that cause you to hyperfocus to your advantage. When I am aware that I am hyperfocusing, I will switch to a task on my to-do list for 15 minutes and then switch back to the original activity. I've found that this sandwiching strategy tricks my brain into focusing on tasks I may otherwise find boring.

Reduce the time you spend on unproductive activities. If you frequently waste time on useless activities that prevent you from prioritizing your homework and other responsibilities, set an alarm clock. Indulge in that activity for a set time. When the alarm goes off, stop that activity. This strategy is especially useful if you spend a lot of time on TikTok and Instagram.

Use your hyperfocus activity as a reward. Use the productive hyperfocus activities you enjoy as rewards for doing the tasks you dislike. This strategy breaks up the monotony of unpleasant tasks and gives you something to look forward to.

Learn how to transition from one task to another. Sometimes your hyperfocus may be so intense that you struggle to transition to another task. I've found that spending 10 minutes on a meditation app can help ease the transition.

Your potential to succeed is infinite!

Turn your ability to hyperfocus into a superpower!

Let's Get Organized

A hectic morning can throw off your whole day. Not only can it be stressful to be rushed in the morning, but being rushed can cause you to forget things. On your way to run out the door, you may forget the English homework you spent hours completing or you may forget your sports kit. Putting a few measures in place to help you get organized can make a world of difference.

Here are a few useful strategies that will help you get organized.

Invest in using a calendar. Spend some time looking for productivity apps, such as 24me, Tidiest, Calendar Today, Calendar, and TickTick that will allow you to create to-do-lists, write notes, and color-coded schedules and download it to your smartphone. Make a habit of adding all your due dates, appointments, and reminders, such as reminders to take your musical instrument or your art supplies to school that day. These apps can be life changers.

Identify and work on problem areas. It may be that you frequently forget to bring your correct textbooks to class, or you don't bring your calculator into school on the days you need them. Whatever your problem area, use your creativity and problem-solving skills to develop a solution and strategy that works for you. I was a disaster when it came to keeping track of my textbooks. Eventually, I decided to buy an extra set of textbooks so that I could keep one set in my school locker and one set at home.

Select your clothes the night before. Whether you wear a school uniform or your own clothes, laying out your outfit the night before can prevent a hectic and stressful morning. It also means that you have one less decision to make and can focus on other things.

Pack your backpack the night before. The evening before school, go through your backpack and take out anything that you don't need for the next day. Once you've finished your homework, put it into your backpack. Make sure you also include any books, folders, pencil cases, stationery, and any other items you will need that day.

Create a space for essentials. Pick a spot where you always put your keys, wallet, water bottle, and anything else you need to have with you. I use a wire basket. Make a habit of putting your things there as soon as you come home so that it's easier to find all your essential items when you have to leave for school.

Leave yourself a sticky note on the front door. If you frequently forget to take something to school, leave yourself a reminder on the front door. For example, if you regularly forget to take your phone charger, leaving yourself a note on the door will mean that you see the reminder as you are about to leave for school.

ORGANIZE YOUR LIFE AROUND YOUR DREAMS, AND WATCH THEM COME TRUE.

TAKE TIME TO DO WHAT MAKES YOU HAPPY.

Chapter 13

PRACTICE SELF-CARE

Practice Self-Care

Being autistic in a world that isn't designed for us is hard. This is made even harder by the fact that we're frequently misunderstood and often don't get the support that we need to flourish in school. It's easy to get caught up in all our problems and difficulties. But dwelling on our problems can get overwhelming and can negatively affect our mental health. By taking care of your physical, emotional and mental health you will be able to have a healthier, happier and more balanced life.

Self-care doesn't have to cost a fortune or be time consuming. Making simple additions to your everyday routine is all that's needed. The beauty of self-care is that there isn't a perfect, correct, or best way to take care of yourself. Your self-care is whatever you need to feel happier and more relaxed. For some people, this may be taking a warm bubble bath while listening to music. For others, it may be spending time in nature. And for others, it may be lighting a beautifully-scented candle, taking an hour to read, or playing chess.

Take time to think about what may help you.

What do you really want to do?

What will help you to rest and refocus?

Below are some tips that you may find helpful.

Treat yourself. One thing that you can control is how you look after yourself. Doing something for yourself every day (big or small) can help you feel better.

Get moving. There are so many benefits to keeping active. Taking part in any form of physical activity releases endorphins, which give you a rush of good feeling. You could join the TikTok dance craze or take your dog for a walk.

Do the things you love. When you're not feeling your best, it can be hard to find the motivation or energy to do what you enjoy. It's at times like this that it's super-important to connect with what you love.

1. Think about the things that make you feel happy and relaxed.

2. Keep doing those things. This could be as simple as watching an episode of your favorite TV show or listening to your favorite songs. It doesn't matter if what you love to do is different from what your friends or anyone else enjoys, as long as it works for you that's all that matters

Build on your strengths. If you're feeling low, focusing on the things you do well can help you feel better about yourself. According to a Gallup study, people who know and work to their strengths are three times as likely to to say that they have an excellent quality of life.

Mindfulness. Mindfulness is about being fully present and engaged in the moment. It requires you to focus on your thoughts and feelings without distractions and judgment. You can do anything mindfully, including eating, walking, baking, singing. Scientific research has shown that mindfulness can reduce stress levels and help people feel more creative, resilient, and focused. There are several apps that can help you get started with mindfulness. For example. ReachOut has an app called 'Breathe,' and there's also the popular 'Smiling Mind' app.

In this chapter, I include lots of self-care activities that I hope you find helpful.

Take A Mini Mental Vacation

Your imagination and creativity are powerful tools you can use to help you to relax, no matter where you are. When a situation becomes too overwhelming, and you need to escape, take a mini-mental vacation.

Do you love the beach? Do you love the gentle sounds of waves, the powdery sand, and the warm breeze?

Do you love being in nature? Do you love hearing the birds chirping and being surrounded by the beauty of flowers and trees?

Do you love snowy winter nights? Do you love huddling in front of a wood-burning stove with a steaming hot chocolate topped with marshmallows?

Take a few minutes, and imagine a place that relaxes you. Use all your senses to go there. If you love a snowy winter day, what does the snow feel like? How does the snow sound when you walk on it? What does the winter day smell like? Can you smell pine or burning wood? How do you feel?

No matter where you are, you can always go on a mini mental vacation.

Create Your Own Sensory Space

Everyone should have a room or space that they can call their own. A soothing and calming haven that you can escape to. When you think about your ideal space, what does it look like? Would you have softer lighting? Would you paint the walls a soothing color? Would you have fluffy pillows and soft blankets? Would you use a diffuser to make your space smell amazing?

Even if you don't have your own room, look for a space to make your own. If you share a room with a sibling, maybe you could make a corner of the room your own by making it cozy and comfortable. Maybe there's a space in a different room that you could use. Even if you don't have your own space, you could have a box filled with objects you find calming that you can use when you need them.

Hang Out With Your Pets

Pets are a great source of comfort and support. If you're fortunate to have a pet, spending time with your pet is a great way to practice self-care. My dog Rico has gotten me through some tough times. When you have a bad day, take your dog for a walk, or cuddle your cat. Play with your guinea pig, hamster, or bunny. Caring for your pets is also an excellent way to shift the focus away from you to caring for your pet. I find that it's a welcome distraction.

Take A Walk (In Nature If You Can)

Nature is a great way to reset and calm yourself. Nature also has a powerful effect on your mental health. If you have access to a park, woods, lake, or garden, resolve to spend more time there. You don't have to be there long. Even a 10-minute walk can make a big difference. Spending time in nature can help to reduce stress, increase positivity and improve your concentration. A study conducted on children with ADHD showed a marked improvement in their concentration after spending 20 minutes in a natural environment.

If you live in a place where you don't have easy access to nature, that's okay. Take a walk around your neighborhood, around your own home, or somewhere that relaxes you.

Tell Yourself Positive Self-Affirmations

Affirmations are statements that you repeat over and over in an attempt to change your unconscious beliefs. Self-affirmations are a great way of practicing self-care because they help to remind us of our positive qualities and the positive aspects of our lives. As we develop the habit of seeing positivity, gratitude, and strength in ourselves, it can help us to develop a more positive view of ourselves.

Below is a list of positive self-affirmations. Select the few that you relate to.

Each day for the next week, select a positive affirmation. In the morning, say the self-affirmation out loud at least five times. Write it down on a sticky note and stick it on your bathroom mirror, on your door or anywhere else you are likely to look at it. Throughout the day, repeat the self-affirmation to yourself in your head. Keep the self-affirmation in the forefront of your mind all day long. Before you go to sleep, repeat the self-affirmation one last time.

- I'm loved.

- I'm strong and brave.

- I'm enough.

- I love myself.

- I respect myself.

- I accept myself.

- I treat myself with kindness.

- I deserve everything that is good.

- I trust myself to make good decisions.

- I don't need to prove myself to anyone.

- I don't need to be perfect.

- I can do anything I set my mind on achieving.

- I focus on the positive.

- I believe in myself.

- I believe that my potential is limitless.

- I know that every problem has a solution.

- I deserve to be happy.

- I'm worth it.

- I enjoy the simple moments.

- I choose to be happy.

- I can and I will.

- I forgive myself for my mistakes.

- It's enough to have done my best.

- Every challenge I face is an opportunity to grow.

- I recognize all the blessings in my life.

- My voice matters.

- I'm the president of my life.

- I'm not afraid of failure.

- I am kind, loving and compassionate.

- I don't compare myself to other people.

- I don't give up when things get difficult.

- I stay true to my values and my authentic self.

Tell Yourself Positive Body Image Affirmations

How do you feel about your body? Do you wish your body looked different? Don't worry; you're not alone. Whether it's television, social media, or the glossy pages of fashion magazines, we are constantly bombarded with unrealistic images and harmful messages about how our bodies should look. It's not surprising that many of us believe that our bodies don't measure up and begin to feel bad about our bodies. Building a positive body image is an excellent way to counteract the negative stream of unattainable images we're encouraged to compare ourselves to.

IN A SOCIETY THAT PROFITS FROM YOUR SELF DOUBT LIKING YOUR BODY IS A REBELLIOUS ACT.

Pick a few affirmations that you like, look in the mirror and repeat them several times each day. If some of these positive body affirmations resonate with you, really allow yourself to see them, hear them, and feel them. You may find that you begin to think differently about yourself and your body.

Tell yourself positive body image affirmations. Developing a positive body image starts with you. Did you know that the things we tell ourselves have a much greater impact than what others say to us? By telling yourself body positive affirmations, you'll be speaking and hearing the affirmative statements that you need to hear to begin to accept and embrace your body.

Here is a list of some positive body image affirmations that you can tell yourself each day.

- "I accept my body the way it is."

- "Other's opinions of my body do not affect or involve me."

- "I deserve to be treated with love and respect."

- "My opinion of myself is the only one that counts."

- "My needs are just as important as anyone else's."

- "I choose to do and say kind things about myself."

- "Not everyone has to like me. I just have to like me."

- "You deserve to love yourself."

- "You deserve to feel comfortable and confident."

- "Being skinny or fat is not my identity. I am identified by who I am on the inside, a loving and wonderful person."

- "I can only go forward, so although I can learn from it, I refuse to dwell on the past."

Make a promise to your body. Make a list of body-positive promises and resolve to stick to them. To get you started, here is a list of some body-positive promises you can make to yourself.

- I will no longer insult you.

- I refuse to compare you to others.

- I'll treat you with love and respect.

- I'll nourish you with healthy foods and lots of water.

- I will keep you strong by remaining active.

- I promise to get enough sleep each night.

Stay Hydrated

You probably already know that drinking water is good for you. The average person should drink at least six to eight glasses of water a day to stay healthy and hydrated.

Although some people love water, it can be pretty boring. If you're tempted to reach for a soda or a fruit drink, give yourself a little self-care by adding some fruit to your water instead. Fruit-infused water can taste delicious and is a healthy way to drink water because you also get the benefits of the antioxidants and vitamin C from the fruit. I love to add lemon slices, strawberries with mint, or raspberries to my water.

How do I make fruit infused water at home?

Start with cold tap or filtered water, then choose a flavor combination you want to use. Some great combinations for fruit-infused water include, lemon and strawberry, strawberry and basil, watermelon and mint, cucumber and mint, and pineapple and ginger.

To prepare, slice ingredients (or tear herbs into large chunks) and add them to the water. The more of an ingredient you use, and the longer you let it infuse, the stronger the flavors will be.

Eat Healthily

What we eat affects how we feel, think, and behave. However, our sensory issues can make it difficult to have a balanced diet. Since many of us are over-sensitive or under-sensitive to smells, tastes, and textures, this can affect our relationship with food and cause anxiety around certain foods. Like many autistic individuals, I'm over-sensitive to taste and smell. I find strong food smells overpowering, which is why I prefer my food to be bland. However, if you are under-sensitive to taste and smell, you may like strong flavors. Most of us are also particular about our food texture, which can further restrict our diet.

Since our diet can elevate our mood, give us more energy, and improve our concentration, you should invest some time in finding creative ways to expand your diet. For example, if you don't like vegetables, try tricking your senses by incorporating them in a fruit smoothie. Try experimenting with the texture of food by modifying it. I puree vegetables and add them to a fruit smoothie or a tomato-based sauce.

Eating at school. I struggled to eat at school. I found the school cafeteria too loud and busy. I also found the social element of eating in a crowded school cafeteria too stressful and overwhelming. If you find the school cafeteria environment is too much for your to handle, ask if you can be allowed to eat in a quiet room away from all the sensory distractions. Being allowed to eat alone in a relaxed and stress-free environment made it much easier for me to eat at school.

Create Your Own Sensory Coping Kit

Our sensory sensitivities can make venturing out into the world scary. Since most autistic individuals are sensitive to noise, smells, touch, lights, and other sensory experiences, it can be incredibly overwhelming to leave the safety of your home knowing that you're going to have to endure an assault to your senses. One coping strategy that I find helpful is to create a sensory coping kit that I can carry with me.

Although I customize my sensory kit to adapt to each situation, my sensory coping kit always has some staple items. I have an extra headset, my sunglasses, airline-style earplugs, antacids, a mint-flavored lip balm, a collection of essential oil rollers (lavender, mint, and lemongrass are firm favorites), a soft hair tie to fiddle with, and scented antibacterial hand gel. I love essential oils because they help mask bad smells; they are also calming and can help you recenter. When it's cold, I may add a hand warmer, and when it's hot, I may add a facial mist.

I recommend you buy a cute makeup bag or large pencil case and fill it with items that will help you cope with the sensory experiences you will experience when you are at school or away from home.

You're Not Alone

No matter how isolated and alone you may feel, I can guarantee that there are other people who've felt exactly like you do right now. When I feel like no one else can relate to what I'm experiencing or how I'm feeling, I do an Internet search to remind myself that other people have gone through what I'm going through. I find comfort in seeing that not only did they survive, they went on to succeed in their chosen profession. Whether it's having debilitating social anxiety, being bullied, battling depression, your parents divorcing, or some other hardship, research two different celebrities who have also gone through this experience. What helped these celebrities to overcome their challenges and setbacks? What have they since gone on to accomplish?

Celebrity:

Hardship:

Accomplishments:

Celebrity:

Hardship::

Accomplishments:

My Coping Tools

We often have to do things or go to places that we would much rather avoid. For example, I find supermarkets really distressing because they overwhelm my senses. I try never to step into one. But sometimes, I have to. You may dislike certain activities or places for similar reasons. Although you may not always be able to avoid these activities and places, you can choose how you respond and behave in these situations. Having a kit of coping tools that I can rely on in stressful situations helps me feel more in control. In the empty boxes below, write down some coping strategies that will help you remain calm.

Think about a safe place.	Breathe in and out slowly.	Ask someone for help.
Count to 40 in intervals of 2s.	**What can I do to help me cope with this situation?**	Play a song in your head.

Get A Good Night's Sleep

A good night's sleep should leave you feeling refreshed, alert, and ready to begin the day. Unfortunately, many autistic individuals have insomnia or poor quality of sleep. Poor sleep quality can affect your memory, concentration, and mood. It can also exacerbate mental health problems, such as anxiety and depression. If you're experiencing any of the following symptoms, you may not be getting the vital rest your body needs:

- Difficulty falling asleep or waking up.

- Frequently waking up during the night.

- Not feeling well-rested when you wake up.

- Feeling tired, sleepy, or drowsy during the day.

- Struggling to focus and perform at school.

ALWAYS REMEMBER TO FALL ASLEEP WITH A DREAM AND WAKE UP WITH A PURPOSE.

Most teens require eight to 10 hours of sleep per night. However, many autistic teens struggle to obtain this. Sleep is regulated by our **circadian rhythm**, an internal body clock that tells us when to feel sleepy and when to feel alert. Many autistic people have a circadian rhythm that's out of synch, making it difficult to have a regular sleeping pattern. Also, teens' internal body clocks are programmed to wake up and go to sleep later, which is why many of us struggle to wake up early for school.

Here are some tips that will help you to improve your sleep:

Create the right bedroom environment. Create a room that's ideal for sleeping. For most people, this means a dark, cool, and quiet bedroom. Try to reduce the amount of light in your room because it can make falling asleep more challenging. If necessary, use room-darkening shades, earplugs, a fan or other devices to create an environment that suits your needs. I highly recommend you invest in a weighted blanket and good quality pillows.

Stick to your schedule. Waking up and going to bed at the same time every day is one of the best ways to beat insomnia.

Limit technology. Sleep experts recommend turning off your phone an hour before bed and silencing your notifications. So, resolve not to use your mobile, iPad, or any other light-emitting screens before bedtime.

Exercise. Exercising and eating well can help you sleep better at night, as long as you don't exercise too late in the day.

Don't eat or drink too close to bedtime. Try to avoid eating big meals too close to bedtime. Drink enough fluid at night to keep from waking up thirsty, but not too much and too close to bedtime that you'll be awakened by needing to go to the bathroom. Also, avoid caffeine because stimulants can disrupt sleep.

Manage your worries. Try to resolve your worries or concerns before bedtime. If you can't, jot down what's on your mind on a piece of paper and then set it aside for tomorrow.

Relax and clear your mind. If stress keeps you up at night, try practicing meditation, listening to calming music, or other relaxation techniques. Many people find that a soothing bedtime routine helps them get sleepy in preparation for bedtime. For example, reading a book and taking a bath. If you find yourself tossing and turning for more than 15 minutes, get up and do an alternate relaxing activity for a while before trying to go to sleep again.

DO SOMETHING TODAY THAT YOUR FUTURE SELF WILL THANK YOU FOR.

Chapter 14

MY FUTURE PLANS

Setting Yourself Up For Success

Setting yourself up for success involves planning for your future. You have already taken the first step by learning more about yourself. The next step is to identify your goals and ambitions. Figuring out your goals and ambitions will help you to find the path you need to take to achieve your goals. One way to figuring our your goals is by asking yourself the following questions.

- What are your interests?

- What do you enjoy doing?

- What are you good at?

- What skills do you have?

It's easy to get overwhelmed by our goals. We've all made many well-intended New Year resolutions only to have them fizzle out and be abandoned. However, a goal is not as much about the outcome but about the journey to achieving it. It's about taking consistent steps towards your goal and making a realistic plan to help you achieve it.

Be specific. Define your goal and how you'll get there. Outline the exact steps you'll take. Instead of, "I want to learn how to code," frame it as, "Every Saturday, I am going to spend an hour teaching myself how to code using resources I find on the Internet."

Make it measurable. Each step should get you closer to your goal. This approach will help to keep you motivated, build momentum, and allow you to track your progress. If you spend one hour every Saturday learning to code, you've succeeded! Then you can step it up by defining the next step you can take to reach your goal. If you find you didn't stick to your goal, keep trying, or re-evaluate. It may turn out that this goal isn't as important to you as you initially thought.

This chapter is designed to get you to think about your future and setting yourself up for success.

My Step Ladder To Success

What is one of your major future goals? Do you want to be an architect? A doctor? An engineer? Whatever your goal, write it in the space below. For each rung of the ladder leading up to your goal, write a small step you can take to help you get closer to reaching your goal. It could be graduating from high school, doing well in a particular class, or whatever else you feel can help you achieve your goal. Never forget that the steps and sacrifices you make now will help you to succeed in the future.

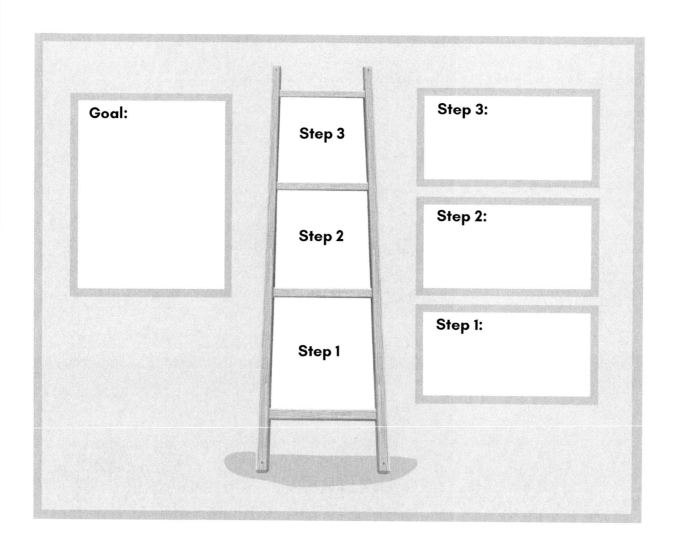

Goal:

Step 3

Step 2

Step 1

Step 3:

Step 2:

Step 1:

Unlocking Solutions

We all face obstacles that stand in the way of our success. The best way to overcome these challenges is to use your creativity to come up with solutions. Below is a lock with a problem and a key containing the answer. Match the key to the appropriate lock. Never forget that your creativity and problem-solving skills are the key to unlocking the solutions to any obstacles you have to overcome.

Someone says something mean to you.

You fail at something.

You're having a hard time focusing.

Resolve to keep trying.

Take a break.

Firmly ask them to stop.

Answer key: Someone says something mean to you = Firmly ask them to stop. – You Fail at something. = Resolve to keep trying. – You're having a hard time focusing = Take a break.

Letter To Your Future Self

Write a letter to your future self. Talk about your goals, dreams, fears, hopes - all of it! Then seal it in an envelope, address it to yourself with a stamp, and give it to your parent or a trusted family member. Ask them to mail it to you one year from that date. When you read it a year later, you'll be surprised at how far you've come.

Dear Future Self,

If you're still feeling anxious or things haven't turned out the way you'd like, think of how far you've come!

Even if you don't have the answers yet, take it one day at a time. Be proud of yourself. You're awesome!

XOXO

GOOD THINGS AHEAD

Who I Am vs. Who I Want To Be

Rate yourself in the following areas.

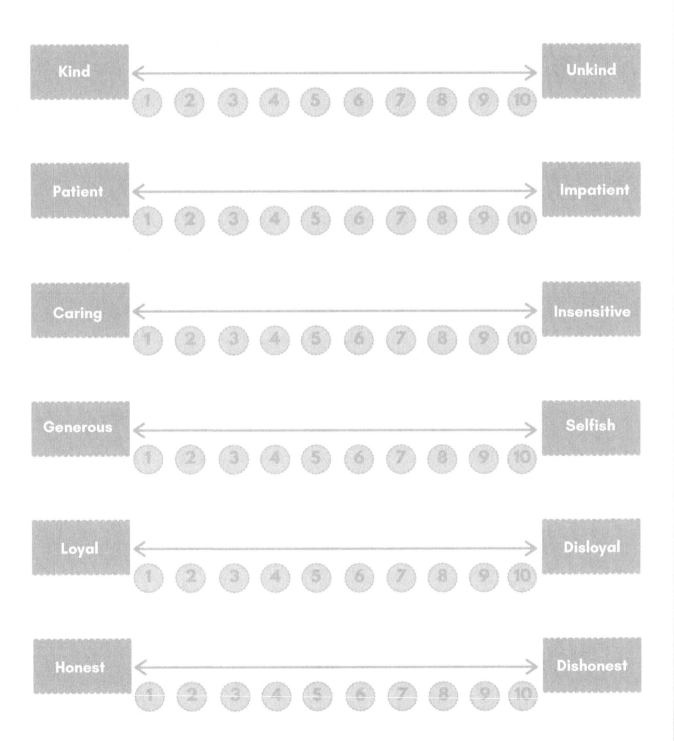

Kind — 1 2 3 4 5 6 7 8 9 10 — Unkind

Patient — 1 2 3 4 5 6 7 8 9 10 — Impatient

Caring — 1 2 3 4 5 6 7 8 9 10 — Insensitive

Generous — 1 2 3 4 5 6 7 8 9 10 — Selfish

Loyal — 1 2 3 4 5 6 7 8 9 10 — Disloyal

Honest — 1 2 3 4 5 6 7 8 9 10 — Dishonest

Pick two of the character traits on the previous page and write about how you can work on increasing the qualities that you aspire to have.

Area 1:

_____

_____

_____

_____

Area 2:

_____

_____

_____

_____

Ingredients For Success

Below are some of the traits that successful people have in common. Circle any of the characteristics that you share with them.

Enthusiastic

Patient

Generous

Fair

Reliable

Supportive

Creative

Kind

Problem-Solver

Brave

Tolerant

Fun

Honest

Hard-Working

Confident

Forgiving

Optimistic

Thoughtful

Determined

Loyal

Focused

Using My Toolbox

It's easy to forget that each of us has the resources to help us overcome any challenges, setbacks, and obstacles that we may face. Sometimes these resources lie within us, and sometimes these resources may be the people in our lives (such as our parents and teachers), or things that we have access to (such as the Internet and our mobile phones). Fill your toolbox below with the resources you already have that can help you to achieve your goals.

Look For Silver Linings

Most of us have a habit of focusing on the things that go wrong in our lives. We may even fall into the trap of focusing on them so often that we begin to see our lives as a never-ending series of setbacks and disappointments. This pessimistic mindset can inadvertently set negative events into motion. Research has shown that looking on the bright side of things when something goes wrong is the most powerful way of dealing with life's inevitable challenges. Being optimistic reduces our stress levels, improves our mental health, and sets us up for success.

How To Look For Silver Linings

Start by listing five things that make your life enjoyable, enriching, or worthwhile. These things can be as general as "I have an awesome dog," or as specific as "I had delicious fluffy pancakes for breakfast this morning." The purpose of this first step is to help you shift into a positive state of mind about your life in general.

Next, think about the most recent time when something didn't go your way or when you felt frustrated, irritated, or upset. In a few sentences, briefly describe the situation below.

_____

_____

_____

_____

Then, list three things that can help you to see the bright side of this situation. For example, you get a detention for repeatedly forgetting to turn in your homework. Three ways to look on the bright side of this situation could be the following.

1. You can use the detention as motivation to come up with a system that helps you to organize yourself so that you don't forget to turn in your homework again.

2. It can serve as a wake-up call to finally ask a teacher or parent for help with your organizational skills.

3. Ten years from now, you're unlikely to remember that you got a detention.

Now It's your turn.

1.

2.

3.

EVERY CLOUD
HAS A SILVER
LINING.

My Future Is Bright

What does success look like to you? Is it doing well in school? Becoming a lawyer, doctor, architect, engineer, journalist, or even an acrobat? Making lots of friends? Having less social anxiety? Identifying your goals is the first step to achieving them. In each space below the light bulb, write a goal you hope to achieve and write down the steps you can take towards getting closer to achieving this goal. For example, if you want to do better in school, steps that will help bring this about could include spending more time studying and asking for help if you're struggling to understand a concept.

_____

_____

_____

_____

Crossing Your Bridge To Happiness

Imagine yourself on one side of this bridge and happiness on the other side. What is blocking you from being able to cross the bridge? Write down the things that are holding you back on the space below the bridge.

_____

_____

_____

_____

_____

BE YOURSELF

BECAUSE AN

ORIGINAL IS

WORTH MORE

THAN A COPY.

Final Thoughts

Congratulations! You made it to the end. I hope you've learned some new coping strategies that will help you manage your sensory issues and anxiety and make it easier for you to make and maintain friendships and succeed in school. Overall, I hope you feel that you're better able to handle all the things life will throw at you.

I want to leave you with some final thoughts.

Life is far from perfect, and that's okay. I've had so many setbacks and devastating disappointments. Sadly, life isn't fair, and it sometimes feels like we always end up with the short end of the stick. I'm so used to having things not go my way and having to overcome so many more obstacles and challenges than other people that I've learned to expect hardships. I'm not going to lie. Sometimes life sucks. It can be <u>really</u> hard and bitterly disappointing to keep having to pick yourself up. But I'm a firm believer that things happen for a reason. Some of my most joyous moments and greatest achievements came from how I dealt with setbacks. Not all storms come to disrupt your life; some clear your path so that you can travel where you are meant to go. I want you to know that you have a beautiful life ahead of you filled with exciting adventures and limitless possibilities. Although you may have more obstacles and challenges than most people your age, never forget that the sweetest victory and the best views come after the hardest climb. I hope you believe in yourself as much as I believe in you and your infinite potential.

Keep shining bright. Keep being you because you're **awesome and autistic!**

There is always something to be happy about.

NOTES

NOTES

NOTES

NOTES